WEATHER TO FISH

(or Game Fishing and the Elements)

Weather to Fish

(or Game Fishing and the Elements)

JACK MEYLER

Thomas Harmsworth Publishing Company
Stoke Abbott

British Library Cataloguing in Publication Data
Meyler, Jack
   Weather to fish : or game fishing and the elements.
   1. Great Britain. Game fishing Angling
   I. Title
   799.12

   ISBN 0–948807–12–1

Typeset by Fox Design, Surbiton

Printed and bound in Great Britain by
Bookcraft (Bath) Ltd

Contents

Diagrams and Tables:

Foreword

When we take up angling we do not fish for many months without learning that weather has a large part to play in our fortunes. Today's weather, for sure: probably yesterday's and last week's. Even tomorrow's, perhaps. Our big difficulty arises when we try, as we must, to work out the whys and wherefores. Weather clearly opens or closes a door standing between us and our pleasure on or by the water, but it never seems to do either in precisely the same fashion twice.

Jack Meyler is a fellow-angler who has given much constructive thought to these matters, writing this book as a result of it. As a World War Two fighter pilot his attention was duly concentrated. What the met. men predicted and how he and his comrades interpreted what they actually found when they arrived up there in the lonely sky was not merely a matter of academic interest. It could be the prime factor which decided whether they would return to earth at the end of a flight alive or dead.

Jack Meyler has not confined his observations to how weather is generated, its bearing on angling prospects and how to exploit or frustrate its contribution to them. He has gone much further. There are few aspects of game fishing at which he has not taken at least a passing look and has in consequence entered areas where controversy is not unknown. His book is none the worse for that display of intrepidity.

D A Orton – editor, *Where to Fish*

Preface

From the outset, I had no intention to write a book, least of all on a technical subject. After all I did not know very much and the word 'expert' did not, and still does not, exist in my vocabulary. I had been taught to fish from an early age and the principles of meteorology then did not come into the picture, only what the ghillies said, and they knew all about their own lochs and rivers. The fact was we caught fish.

The first confrontation with meteorological (met) theory came with the war. To do the job I wanted to do, to 'drive' aeroplanes, it was necessary, inter alia, to pass the met. exams and I suppose that is where it all began, (and this has been touched upon under Fishing and Flying later in the book).

After the war, first as an accountant in industry, in private practice and later in commerce, it was a few years before I could afford time for fishing, with a young family to help bring up. Nevertheless, I did get back to fishing and, after some years, to aviation as a flying instructor in The Channel Islands and, of course, meteorology was one of the subjects I had to teach. I learned much, 'As by your pupils you'll be taught' – very true, and here I am trying to reconcile art and craft with science, and neither, of course, very exact. However, I owe a considerable debt to friends who have given encouragement and assistance and I also wish to acknowledge my appreciation to the authors of several books who have corrected some of the inaccuracies in my text. To my many fishing friends, for their contributions, I say 'Thank you' as indeed I do to Dr Jack Goodier for casting a scientific eye over the text. I have enjoyed putting all this together and trust that this little book will give some pleasure and instruction in return.

Prologue

'The proper fly properly presented at the proper time generally brings forth the proper result.' This masterpiece of pedantry is affectionately attributed to William Lunn, for many years Head Bailiff of The Houghton Club at Stockbridge, Hampshire, on the River Test.

J W Hills records this quotation in his book *River Keeper*, based upon Lunn's life as an accomplished naturalist and fisherman. As to 'The Proper Fly', exhaustive studies are already recorded in innumerable works on that fascinating subject by authors more experienced than the writer and, in any case, outside the scope of this little book. To present the fly 'properly at the proper time' requires patience, observation, some knowledge and a little experience, to find out where and at what depth the fish are feeding or taking. This is no easy matter at the best of times, unless the fish are taking hatching flies or spent spinners on the surface or nymphs in the surface film.

In these cases the rise form can be seen and the position of the feeding fish is known. At other times, the water appears quite devoid of fish, but they are surely there, somewhere. A little more knowledge as to the manner in which insect life and fish behaviour is affected by the elements will not only help the game fisherman, whether he be tyro or experienced angler, to find the fish but will also bring more enjoyment to a sport which on occasions is reduced, unfortunately, to the practice of 'chuck and chance', not to mention valuable time wasted in 'thrashing' unproductive water. The size of the bags must, now, surely improve, so that the 'proper result' can be more easily, more often and more pleasurably brought forth.

'Simon Peter saith unto them, I go a fishing. They say unto him, we also go with thee.'

John XXI 3

CHAPTER 1

INTRODUCTION

The basic elements

The basic elements as we were taught them at school, were Air, Earth, Water and Fire. The word 'Elements' has, however, over the years come to mean all the various factors making up our weather, which may be described as the science of the air.

The Chapters which follow, therefore, seek to include all the elemental factors affecting Game Fishing.

Although it was with some difficulty that anything constructive or even relevant to the subject could be included about the element, Earth, it is nevertheless hoped that a later chapter will give just sufficient light-hearted relief from that rather serious subject, Weather.

A later chapter, on Fire, covers various effects the sun's heat and light (and also shadow) have upon the sport. Although a cold body, which only reflects the light of the sun, the moon's effects are included with a short discourse on the solunar theory.

Although not one of the basic elements in itself (but only a scientific element, as it were) and just a small but most vital constituent part of the basic element, Air, oxygen is considered such a crucial factor affecting fish behaviour that a separate chapter has been devoted to the subject. That chapter considers the oxygen effect upon salmon, diurnally, seasonally and under varying weather conditions.

1

Game fish defined

Game fish in this book include:

Atlantic salmon	*(Salmo salar)*
Brown trout and Sea trout	*(Salmo trutta)*
Rainbow trout	*(Salmo gairdneri)*

All the above belong to the one family, *salmonidae*.

There appears to be only one species of Atlantic salmon. If there are others the author is not aware of them. Land-locked salmon of New Brunswick and Nova Scotia may be a sub-species.

The Pacific salmon is of a different genus, *Onchorhynchus*, and has several species with which these notes are not concerned.

Although no other sea trout species is known than Salmo trutta, the sea trout is named differently in various parts of the British Isles:

Scotland	Herling
Scottish Highlands	Finnoch
Wales	Sewin

These names are restricted to fish of 0.5 lb to 1.0 lb:

Ireland	White trout
Devon	Peal

Our ladies

References to fishermen or the use of certain masculine pronouns are all deemed also to refer to the female of the Homo species, *sapiens*.

There are, of course, many expert and dedicated lady fishermen – 'fisherperson', like 'chairperson', sounds clumsy – and there is no intention that the ladies shall be excluded. Fishing has been, is, and hopefully always will be, a unisex sport. After all, there was Miss Ballantine and her record-breaking salmon.

The British Record (Rod Caught) Fish Committee has recognised the 64lb salmon hooked in the Boat Pool of the Glendelvine water of the river Tay at 6.15pm on 7th October 1922 and landed half a mile below at 8.05pm The fish took a spinning bait, a dace. Its length was 54in and its girth, 28½in and a cast of it is set up at Glendelvine. This salmon is the largest of its species caught by a lady. Personally, I like to see the ladies enjoying their fishing and I enjoy their company in a boat or by the river. They do, of course, provide excellent packed lunches for such occasions.

These occasions, however, are not always the relaxing ones we make them out to be. I remember once on the Shiel in Scotland when my wife left the scene of operations in a huff after I got upset: she was making a rather poor attempt to net for me a good sea trout which I swear was every ounce of 7lb – and I lost it! Later in the day, I lost another, but smaller fish, similarly at the net, trying to be a 'big head' showing her how it should be done. After that, all was forgiven.

Game fish, their behaviour and metabolism.

Although each of the species discussed earlier shares the same generic name, *salmo* there are wide differences in their lifestyles and habits.

The salmon and sea trout are migratory, quite unlike the brown trout which, apart from occasional expeditions into estuarine waters, is confined to freshwater. Some rainbow trout have migratory instincts and all rainbows can withstand higher water temperatures than brown trout. Salmon and sea trout feed and grow in the sea after leaving the rivers as smolts (about 6-8in long).

On returning to freshwater to spawn the salmon is quite unable to digest food because the instincts of reproduction and self preservation take over to the complete exclusion of feeding. In fact by the time the salmon has entered fresh water the reproductive organs have enlarged and the digestive organs diminished.

The sea trout does, however, feed in freshwater, if only to a limited extent, but in succeeding chapters will be treated with the salmon; and the rainbow trout with brown trout together as 'trout'.

What does make a salmon take an artificial fly or bait has not altogether been established, but it is generally accepted that the reasons are associated with curiosity, reflex action and aggression or frustration. The lure appears to the salmon as a normal image, an illusion or silhouette or a combination of them depending upon the light conditions and the pattern and size of fly used.

The trout take imitations and semi-imitations of their natural food at times, inter alia, when the insecta upon which they feed are hatching or are otherwise available.

There is no doubt that the behaviour of all salmo species is affected by the elements. The salmon have their taking times and these seem generally to coincide with the feeding times of trout, despite the differing lifestyles of the different species in freshwater. Conditions suitable for the hatching of early upwinged duns, such as March brown *(Rhithrogena harrupi)* and large dark olive *(Baetis rhodani)* also seem right to make salmon active enough to take an artificial bait.

At other times, usually when there is no hatch of insects, the fish repair to deep water and remain quite inactive and unresponsive. To appreciate just how the elements affect the habits and behaviour of the fish, it is necessary to understand their metabolism, the rate of which is affected by the body temperature which in turn is acquired from the water, because fish are cold-blooded, unlike mammals and birds.

A critical rise in the temperature of the water increases the rate of metabolism and will also give rise immediately to an increase in the availability of dissolved oxygen in the water and the amount of oxygen absorbed for respiration. It is at such times that the fish will become more active and mentally

4

alert and, if only for a short period, will come on the take. It must be added, though, that this beneficial effect ceases when water temperatures rise above 70°F.

An insufficiency of oxygen, and indeed an excess availability, will make the fish lethargic and indifferent.

In considering the various elements affecting the available supply of oxygen to the fish, it is intended to take each element and each constituent of weather separately and to trace their effect, inter alia, on water temperature; to consider intermediate conclusions at that stage; to discuss oxygen; and then ultimately to summarise final conclusions.

'. . . and first for the Element that I use to trade in, which is the Air, an element of more worth than weight, an element which doubtless exceeds both the Earth and Water.' Auceps

The First Day – *The Compleat Angler*
Izaak Walton (1593-1683)

CHAPTER 2

AIR (WEATHER)

General

Fishing and Flying

During the latter part of the Second World War the author was a young squadron pilot in fighter command of the Royal Air Force, mostly stationed in Britain. Apart from periods of operational necessity, when high-powered aeroplanes were flown at great altitudes, and at great speeds for those days, there were periods of so-called rest, when lighter aeroplanes were flown (such as Tiger Moths and Austers) to transport senior officers from one place to another. These flights were nevertheless considered to be of operational necessity, although of lower priorities and included mess parties and dances or conferences.

Many of these trips, particularly over the West country and Scotland, depending upon where the squadron was stationed at the time, covered areas which in pre-war days contained great game fishing potential. On such occasions the thoughts of the once fly-fishing pilot (when at low altitudes because of weather exigencies, of course) strayed from the urgencies of the matter immediately in hand to the more relaxing thoughts of trout streams and salmon and sea trout rivers and lochs. It was from about 500 feet above ground level that one could best observe and appreciate the waters, where, as a boy, one had been taught the basic principles of fly fishing, almost regardless of actual weather eventualities.

In Scotland, at any rate, conditions were either sound or dour, depending upon the judgement of the ghillie at the time. The instruction was good: how to approach the water, sunshine and shadow and how not to put fish down, where the lies were, how to cast, which flies or baits to use, why fly size was, perhaps, more important than choice of pattern. But only little instruction was received on the elements.

And so it was with flying. None less than the flying instruction, the ground instruction was excellent – how to keep fit, physically and mentally, about hygiene, administration, pilot navigation, armament, aircraft engines and systems, wireless telegraphy (morse), radio telephony, aircraft, ship and tank recognition and lastly and leastly meteorology – mainly concerned with visibility, or the lack of it, winds and cloud.

The writer and his young friends flew in those days on very sketchy met. reports and forecasts. If the weather on the proposed route or in the area, say, of an operational sweep, was reasonably clear, and the lowest cloud-base not too low, and with no immediate foreseeable hazard, the flight proceeded. If otherwise, the pilots were temporarily grounded until conditions improved. These decisions were usually accepted without any beefing. The elements were nevertheless of paramount importance to all types of flying, operational and domestic, since the replacement of a lost aeroplane and pilot would cost the war effort a lot of money.

But the elements, as relating to game fishing as such, had rarely been considered even by ghillies of great experience and reputation. They made their assessments of weather and water conditions upon common sense and folklore, passed from one generation to another. Many of these assessments were well-founded, and can now be explained scientifically having regard to modern meteorological knowledge, which was not very advanced before the Second World War when the art of flying and this science were only just starting to gain in importance, both from a rather slow beginning. So fishing and flying do have much in common, and the common factor is the elements.

It is therefore with some diffidence that the writer has perhaps broken new ground in an attempt to bring together the art of fishing and the science of the elements, particularly Air, and in some detail, Weather. Art and science are separately fascinating in themselves but positively connected by cause and effect. There is always a reason why game fish (indeed all animals) behave the way they do and there can be no doubt whatsoever that they are influenced by elemental conditions, which to a great extent means weather. With this in mind the writer has embarked, if somewhat boldly, upon this work and, in particular, the remainder of this rather technical chapter.

Meteorology – the study of the weather

It is well known that the weather plays a leading part in the success or otherwise of a fishing expedition, but less so are the reasons why certain conditions produce better sport than others.

Most anglers, before setting out, will tap the barometer and read or hear the weather forecast and perhaps study the current weather map (or isobaric chart) in the daily newspaper, if only to ascertain the direction and strength of the forecast surface winds. To understand fully the effects our variable weather has upon the fish it will be helpful to have some basic knowledge of elementary met., and for convenience this has been dealt with under the headings which follow:

Constitution of the air

The air is made up of a variety of colourless gases, the main constituents being oxygen (about a fifth) nitrogen and very small amounts of other gases such as argon, carbon dioxide, hydrogen and helium. Water vapour (moisture) is, of course, also present.

This gaseous envelope which encircles the earth extends to only approximately 200 miles above the surface, becoming rarer as one goes higher. To appreciate how very thin the air becomes even relatively close to the earth's surface: in the absence of pressurised air conditioning, the use of a supplementary oxygen supply becomes mandatory for air crews at about 10,000 feet above mean sea level (amsl).

Temperature and its effects upon water and upon fish

Air is warmed indirectly by the sun's rays (solar radiation) striking the earth which warms, by conduction, the air in contact with it. Warm air being less dense and, therefore, lighter than cooler air, rises; convection currents are set up and continue in an endeavour to equate the temperature of the air close to the earth's surface.

As one ascends above the earth's surface, so the temperature decreases at a lapse rate of approximately 2°(C) per 1,000 feet. (This rate varies depending upon whether the air is stable or unstable.) The exception to this is in the not-unusual condition of a temperature inversion whereby a volume of warm air is trapped below stratus cloud, and floats above a layer of cold air, which usually turns into thick fog.

A pocket thermometer is a very useful instrument to carry in one's kit in order to be able to measure:

(a) the ambient air temperature (in the shade), and
(b) the water temperature (at about 1 foot below the surface).

Usually during the hours of daylight, in spring and early summer, the water is cooler than the air and, in that respect, conditions are right for fish to feed or 'take' on or just below the surface. (The word 'take' is used here to include the salmon which, as previously discussed, does not feed in fresh water.)

But the angler will have observed that sometimes, on late summer evenings after a warm day and a cloudless sky, with a very light breeze and rapid earth-cooling into space (terrestrial radiation), the surface and immediate sub-surface rises of trout abruptly cease (particularly a buzzer or a sedge rise) (usually as the sun goes down when, in normal conditions, the cream of the day's fishing could be expected for another hour until after dark). The air temperature has in fact become cooler than that of the water, which, we must have experienced, feels warm to the hand. When, as is possible in those conditions, a thin layer of radiation mist starts to form over the river valley or surface of the lake, we know that productive fishing is all over bar the shouting. The fish have gone down to lie in deeper water, since the chilling of the water surface adversely affects them. With a little foresight and patience it can be predicted when the air temperature will fall considerably at sunset to the air's dewpoint temperature – bad news – so accordingly we pack up fishing. It is useless to continue. ('Dewpoint temperature' and 'radiation mist' are covered in greater detail later in this chapter.)

What in fact has happened is that the surface of the water has been cooled to a temperature below that which encourages the hatching of insects. When there is no feed on the surface the fish will move to deeper water to seek their supply of food. In any case, the convection currents set up by the surface cooling are felt in the lateral lines of the fish (a sensitive part of their nervous system) causing some considerable discomfort, particularly when cruising just below the surface. (Seasonal changes in water temperature are discussed more fully later.)

The writer has caught rainbows in Lake Charlotte, British Columbia, a lake fed from melting mountain snows, at water temperatures of about 41°F (5°C) and in a dam at Dulstroom, Natal, where the water temperature was taken at 77°F (25°C).

It is well established that up to 42°F (6°C) salmon can be fairly dour since their metabolic rate is low. At 42°F (6°C), a salmon will go through white water below a weir and mount the fall. Between 42°F (6°C) and 48°F (9°C) a salmon will not stir far to intercept an artificial fly and indeed a bait must be dragged past its nose for it to move to take it. At 48°F (9°C) and over it is established that a salmon will rise to an artificial fly, the size of fly required depending upon the water temperature, colour and flow.

The trout, in general, also awakens from its metabolic state of rest as the water temperature rises, and progressively increases its food intake. It is, of course, the temperature of the water, rather than that of the air alone which increases the metabolic rate and which is so important for the activity and alertness of the fish.

This thermometer formula will be found to be useful:

	Freezing	Boiling
Fahrenheit (F)	32°	212°
Centigrade (C)	0°	100°

$F = \frac{9}{5}(x + 32)$ — [where x = the number of degrees (C)]
$C = \frac{5}{9}(y - 32)$ — [where y = the number of degrees (F)]

Relative humidity

The temperature of the air reaches what is called its dewpoint when it is cooled to saturation. Warm air holds more water vapour than does cold air and the relative humidity is the amount of water vapour in the air, compared with that in saturated air, and is expressed as a percentage. Saturated air is therefore 100% humid and is evidenced by cloud, fog, mist, rain, snow, dew or hoar-frost (precipitation). The air then can be likened to a sponge which, with relative humidity of somewhat less than 100%, will continue to take in water vapour until it becomes saturated. Unsaturated air takes in water vapour from a water surface by means of evaporation. But because heat is needed to convert water from a liquid to a gaseous state, latent heat is extracted from the water to make

11

the change. So when water evaporates, the surface becomes cooler and, as mentioned earlier, this can be very off-putting to the fish which sense the change. Their metabolic rate slows down and they tend to lie inactive in deeper water.

Most of us are aware that a good soft growing day for the gardener is also a potentially productive day for the fisherman. But a good hard drying day for the housewife is bad news for the exponent of the angle and there will be no limit-bags. To ascertain the relative humidity of the air, it is necessary to take a reading from a hygrometer, to learn whether the dry air flow from the south-east, for example, although not cold in itself in mid-summer, will evaporate the surface of the loch to any degree and also cool it, to the detriment of the fishing, or at best, prevent a normal daytime rise in water temperature. The hygrometer will not look good to the fisherman below 85%, nor indeed at 100% when precipitation will be likely. (Meteorological 'nut cases' have been known, however, to include a small light hygrometer in the fishing gear!) As regards humidity, apart from relative humidity, it may be convenient to record at this stage a simple table of air temperatures and their average contents of moisture or water vapour, bearing in mind that warm air can hold more moisture than cold air.

Air temperature	Moisture per cubic foot of air.
30°F (-1°C)	2 grams
50°F (10°C)	4 grams
90°F (32°C)	15 grams

Barometric pressure

The weight of a column of air above the earth is about 14.5lb per square inch and is called atmospheric or barometric pressure, being measured in inches of mercury or in millibars, by means of a mercury or aneroid barometer. Standard mean sea level (msl) pressure is fixed at 29.92 in or 1013.2 millibars, but of course pressure does vary according to actual conditions. Standard msl pressure has no application in game fishing and is used in flying for purposes of flight separation and to fix flight levels above a standard msl datum point. Barometric pressure, in general, decreases with altitude at about 1 millibar for every 30 feet.

High pressure is associated with fair and settled weather and low pressure with bad weather, with wind and rain and unsettled conditions generally. Apart from the actual weather associated with high or low pressures, the trends are more important than the actuals. Sustained periods of either very high or very low pressure are not good for game fishing, as the fish tend to become inactive and lack mental alertness.

With a high or rising barometer there is a greater or increasing pressure of air on the water, the surface of which takes in oxygen from the air, even up to the point of supersaturation. This in turn makes more oxygen available for the fish's respiration and has the effect, all other factors being equal, of tending to increase the activity and mental alertness of the fish. An excessive availability of oxygen, however, will have a different effect, making the fish heady but not limiting their physical activity.

With a low or falling barometer there is reduced or decreasing pressure of air on the water, the surface of which gives off oxygen to the air. Less oxygen in this case is available for the fish which now seek deeper water and become less active and mentally alert.

A change in barometric pressure is therefore needed to shake the fish out of their inactive state. The commencement of an upward trend from a low or a downward trend from a high is sufficient, generally, to achieve this.

It must not, however, be overlooked (and as discussed in previous subsections of this chapter) that there are other variable weather factors, such as relative humidity and air temperature which affect water temperature and therefore the amount of dissolved oxygen available for the salmon's respiration. Similar variable conditions affect the habits of water

13

insecta, especially the metamorphosis of nymphs into sub-imagines (duns) or pupae into adult flies, in the case of buzzer *(Diptera)* or sedge *(Trichoptera)* and, therefore, the feeding habits of the trout. Barometric trends should be studied in connection with air temperature and wind direction.

A too rapid rise in barometric pressure usually portends unsettled windy weather (as, of course, does a rapid fall).

A rising barometer with:

(a) a falling thermometer brings less wind or a light north easterly wind, mostly in winter,

(b) a veering wind (changing direction clockwise), say, from south to west, brings fair cooler weather,

(c) a rising thermometer brings fine weather and light winds, and a high pressure area (anti-cyclone) is approaching.

A falling barometer with:

(a) a backing wind (changing direction anti-clockwise), say, from south to south-east, brings unsettled weather and rain, and a low pressure area (cyclone) is approaching,

(b) a rising temperature brings rain and southerly wind,

(c) a falling temperature brings snow and northerly winds, possibly strong.

Barometric pressure tends to remain high over the poles and low over the equator throughout the year.

A ridge of high pressure indicates a short spell of fine weather with good visibility, followed usually by deteriorating conditions.

A trough of low pressure indicates a short period of unsettled weather with rain and high winds.

NORTHERN HEMISPHERE PRESSURE SYSTEMS

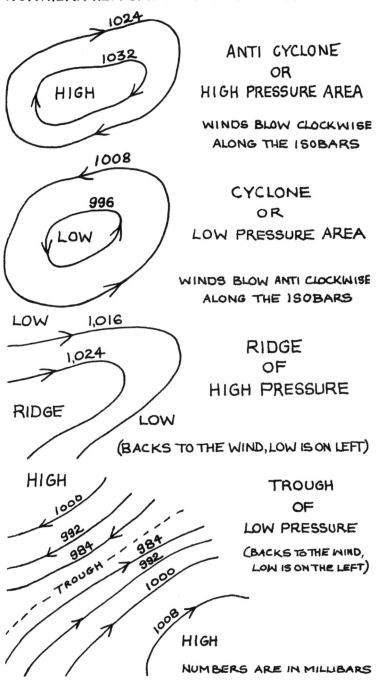

1024

1032

HIGH

ANTI CYCLONE
OR
HIGH PRESSURE AREA

WINDS BLOW CLOCKWISE
ALONG THE ISOBARS

1008

996

LOW

CYCLONE
OR
LOW PRESSURE AREA

WINDS BLOW ANTI CLOCKWISE
ALONG THE ISOBARS

LOW   1,016

1,024

RIDGE

LOW

RIDGE
OF
HIGH PRESSURE

(BACKS TO THE WIND, LOW IS ON LEFT)

HIGH

1000

992

984   984
        992

TROUGH

1000

1008

HIGH

TROUGH
OF
LOW PRESSURE

(BACKS TO THE WIND,
LOW IS ON THE LEFT)

NUMBERS ARE IN MILLIBARS

'When I have told the readers that . . .; and that if he be an honest Angler the east wind may never blow when he goes a fishing.'

Epistle to the Reader – *The Compleat Angler*
Izaak Walton (1593-1683)

Wind

Pressure systems and isobars

Wind is the movement of air over and above the earth's surface and is caused by a combination of factors. In general:

(a) differences in barometric pressure,

(b) differences in temperature between one latitude and another,

(c) the rotation of the earth – approx 360° in 24 hours.

Because of (c) above, winds do not blow directly from a high pressure area (anti-cyclone) to a low pressure area (cyclone) but, at 2000 feet above mean sea level clear of all ground obstructions, winds blow along the isobars. These are lines on a weather map (isobaric chart) joining together places of equal barometric pressure at a given time. Winds in the northern hemisphere blow clockwise around a high and anti-clockwise around a low pressure area and conversely in the southern hemisphere. An anti-cyclone usually moves very slowly and a cyclone rapidly. Because of ground obstructions, surface winds blow in a direction of about 25° inclined towards the low pressure areas.

Buys Ballot's Law

Many years ago, a Dutchman, named Buys Ballot, established that an observer in the Northern Hemisphere, with his back to the wind, will have the low pressure area on his left, and conversely in the Southern Hemisphere.

16

Thermal winds

Land masses on or near the equator, with the sun directly overhead, heat up more quickly than do those in northern or southerly latitudes where the rays of the sun are not so direct. Warm air, being less dense than cold air, will rise and form areas of low pressure over the equatorial land regions, where at the same time, to the north and to the south of the equator, the air above the cooler land forms areas of higher pressure. Here again, the winds will not blow directly from high to low but because of the effect of the rotation of the earth, the 2000 feet winds will blow along the isobars. These are called thermal winds, and can either be seasonal (isobaric winds) or diurnal (sea and land breezes).

Sea and land breezes

As land heats up and cools down more quickly than does water, on sunny days, areas of lower pressure are formed over land and high pressure over the sea. On these occasions, in late afternoon, purely local winds will blow from sea to land and these are called sea breezes, and may extend inland some miles and up into river valleys. At night, after the land has cooled down somewhat, the reverse will apply and toward dawn, winds called land breezes will blow from land to sea.

Surface winds

The winds below 2000 feet are considerably modified both in speed and direction by ground features such as mountains, hills, buildings and trees, which cause inconsistent wind velocities, called gusts. Wind velocity (as against wind speed alone) is a vector which includes both speed and direction. The surface winds, as compared with the isobaric winds, will be about 20% reduced in strength over land and somewhat less reduced over the sea. As regards direction, the surface winds

17

will have backed (changed direction anti-clockwise) about 25° over land, inclining more towards the low pressure area and less so over the sea where there is less surface obstruction.

Other local winds

There are also other types of local winds near the earth's surface caused by geographic features. Anabatic winds blow up the sides of mountains and on other occasions Katabatic winds blow down the sides of mountains at times when the tops are snowcapped. There are other local winds (for instance the Mistral and Chinouk).

Basic knowledge required

It is really only necessary for the fisherman to understand basically how winds arise, how pressure areas are formed and move, usually from a westerly to an easterly direction (due to the earth's rotation) and to ascertain from the weather maps the disposition of pressure areas. The barometric pressure trends and weather tendencies, generally, can be roughly forecast and surface wind velocities predicted, as can the veering or backing of local winds.

Veering and backing winds

The direction of a wind is the direction from which it blows. A veering wind will change direction clockwise and will increase in terms of the points of the compass, for example, from south (180°) to south-west (225°). A backing wind will change direction anti-clockwise and will decrease in terms of the points of the compass, for example, from north-west (315°) to west (270°).

Pressure gradient

The closer together the isobars are on a weather map, the stronger the wind; conversely, weaker when further apart. This is called the pressure gradient.

Upper winds

Upper winds such as jet streams do not really concern this treatise, although an observation as to the speed and direction of high cloud will usually give evidence as to the main air flow at the time, and possibly for the immediate future, of surface winds.

Wind measurement

The method of recording wind speed is usually by means of a cup anemometer which senses the pressure of the wind and translates the information electronically on to a calibrated screen, the speed in mph or knots, not only the steady wind speed but also lulls and gusts. Wind direction is, in general, ascertained by a weather vane which points in the direction from which the wind is blowing. One simple warning, however: never trust a wind anemometer or vane unless they are placed sufficiently high up to avoid turbulence caused by ground obstructions.

There are other anemometers which in addition record wind strengths in forces according to an internationally accepted scale, the Beaufort Scale which is recorded on the following page.

Air masses

Winds usually acquire the properties of the surface whence they arise and over which they are blown. A south-westerly wind from the south Atlantic Ocean (Tropical Maritime Air) is

19

relatively warm depending upon the season of the year, and mostly moist; whereas a north westerly from the Arctic Regions (Polar Maritime Air) is cold and mostly moist and can bring snow in winter. A south-easterly from southern Europe and north Africa (Tropical Continental Air) has little water to cross and is usually warm and dry in summer and cooler in winter. Lastly a north easterly or easterly wind from the frozen wastes of Siberia (Polar Continental Air) becomes cold and dry in winter and cool and dry in summer. These are mainly generalisations. There are, of course, exceptions and combinations of winds arising from different air masses during the various seasons of the year.

Beaufort scale

Force	Indications	Approx speed in mph
0	Flat calm, smoke goes up straight flag on flag pole hangs limply	0
1	light airs causing slight ripple, smoke slants, flag blows out lightly	2
2	light breeze, wind felt on face, flag flutters briskly	5
3	gentle breeze when leaves are moved, flag flies out straight	10
4	moderate breeze, bushes sway, flag pole sways a little	15
5	fresh breeze, tree tops sway, white horses on lakes	20
6	strong breeze, trees sway, wind whistles through the telephone lines	25
7	moderate gale, whole trees move	30
8	gale, twigs broken from trees	35
9	strong gale, minor damage to houses (chimney pots and tiles)	40
10	whole gale, trees uprooted, major damage to houses	45
11	storm, widespread damage	55
12	hurricane, severe destruction	60

How to use wind to the best advantage when game fishing

The direction of the wind on a loch, lough, lake or reservoir is most important because it is that which determines the direction of a drifting boat, and from which position on the bank or from which side of a river one starts to fish. Of course, there are other considerations, such as sunshine and shadow, and these will be covered in a later chapter.

Fish will generally move towards areas into which their food supply is being blown and after a sustained wind from one direction, the fish can be found feeding on a lee shore so that a good drift would be into that shore. A good place on the bank from which to fish would be from a promontory or point, preferably across the wind, which would obviate the necessity of casting directly into it. It must, however, be borne in mind that a normal 17 foot fishing boat with bows and a flat stern will not necessarily drift parallel to the wind direction because of the extra freeboard on the bows acting as a sail. The boat will therefore drift slightly stern first and about 20% out of wind, depending upon the strength of the wind and the loading of the boat – a useful tip when positioning a boat before commencing a drift. The actual direction of a drift, therefore, can be altered up to about 40° (20° out of wind each way) simply by turning the boat through 180°. This can be further modified by one or two gentle pulls of the oar, kept in the water, on the windward side, to maintain the boat on the desired drift.

Another means of controlling the speed of the drift in a moderate wind is by putting out a drogue on a rope about 5 yards long (a sizeable plastic bucket with a 3 inch diameter hole cut out of the bottom will also do). A dragging anchor may also be used with care. A further means of controlling the direction of the boat's drift in a light to moderate wind is by the use of a lee board, clamped to the leeward side of the gunwale over the bows. The size of the board would be about 5 foot by 9 inches by .75 inches. This would give the boat extra drag on the leeward

21

side to alter the direction of the drift. This device can, at times, be more trouble than it is worth. Some wind, when not excessive, is a definite advantage for boat fishing because a good ripple or a small wave breaks up the surface of the water and the light, thus distorting the vision of the fish. No fisherman likes a flat calm, not even for dry fly fishing, because the fish can see every movement, the flies look like hooks of iron with feathers tied on them and the line and leader appear more like a telegraph pole floating across the surface of the water. Needless to state, the fish are easily put down. A ripple or a wave also has the effect, amongst other things, of oxygenating the surface of the water, since a rough water surface will obviously take in more air than a smooth surface.

A force 4 or 5 wind producing white horses on the surface is not a good wind for fishing, particularly if the air flow is at all gusty. A dark scudd which sweeps across the surface on a squally day, as over a field of standing hay, is also bad and these conditions can put the fish down deep.

There again, after such rough and gusty conditions have abated, usually towards early evening, scum or calm lanes appear on the surface of the water parallel to the wind direction. The trout, particularly rainbows which are voracious feeders, will move up-wind in the lanes, taking the food, mainly drowned insecta or spent spinners trapped in the white foam each side of the scum lanes. Calm lanes, without necessarily the scum, can appear at any time after a considerable drop in the wind speed. In each of these situations it is necessary to hold the boat in position with the oars, one side or other of the calm lane, keeping on a steady drift.

Casting at 90° to the longitudinal axis of the boat, that is straight ahead down wind, is not always beneficial. If it is possible and with respect to the partner in the boat, casts should be made slightly across wind. As the fish will usually be facing into wind, more fish will be covered on a broader front.

When, sometimes, the wind moderates just before sunset, a good spot to position the boat for a slow drift is near a windward shore, perhaps along a promontory or point, where the air may be that little bit warmer for the start of the late evening rise.

A good position in which to spend the last hour before darkness can be approaching a leeward shore, into a bay or across a point. In all cases, it is, of course, bad fishing ethics to allow a boat to drift to a position, say, less than 100 metres from where bank anglers are fishing.

A few sayings based upon folklore

(a) There is no doubt about it, an easterly wind is bad for fishing. It is not wholly the wind, however, which is, nevertheless, usually dry, but also the strong light and other conditions of the atmosphere.

(b) A veering wind will die away and portends settled weather.

(c) A backing wind will increase and portends unsettled weather.

(d) A strong wind from the north will die down sooner than a strong wind from the south.

(e) In Ireland it is said that when the sky is dark and heavy in 'the butt' of the wind, the wind will strengthen and continue.

(f) And conversely, when the sky is light and clear in 'the butt' of the wind, the wind will die down.

(g) The wind increases when clouds pass over the sun.

(h) When a strong wind is blowing and sun comes out, the wind will reduce. 'The sun kills the wind,' as they say.

(i) When the clouds seem to be moving against the surface wind on land and in wet and windy conditions, the rain and wind will soon abate.

(j) When the clouds are moving against the surface wind on land in fine weather, there will be a change to squally weather.

The merits of the winds from the four cardinal points of the compass can perhaps be summed up in the words of the anonymous poet as follows:

> When the wind is in the east, 'tis neither good for man nor beast;
> When the wind is in the north, I rarely sally forth,
> When the wind is in the west, then 'tis the very best;
> But when the wind is in the south, it blows the 'bait'
>   right into the fish's mouth.

From J O Hallinwell, *Popular Rhymes* (1849)

The poet, whoever he was, knew a thing or two, because the truth of this little verse is, in fact, borne out by the principles of relative humidity, water temperature and the water's dissolved oxygen content available to the fish, of which more in later chapters.

> When ye see a cloud rise out of the west, straightway, ye say, there cometh a shower; and so it is.

St Luke XII 54

Cloud

Cloud is formed when moist air is cooled to its dewpoint temperature (100% relative humidity) and is the first stage in the formation of rain. Depending upon the stability of the air, whether it is dry or saturated and its ability to maintain its state up to certain altitudes, cloud formations, very generally speaking, fall into three main types; Cirrus, Cumulus and Stratus. Cirrus (mare's tails) is a high cloud composed mainly of ice crystals, which can also be in a layer – cirro-stratus – or in puffy form as cirro-cumulus (mackerel sky). These clouds, which can extend from 10,000 feet up to over 50,000 feet are of little concern to the game fisherman, except as a portent of unsettled weather, when cirro-cumulus cloud is packed together. When dispersed loosely fine weather may be expected. Cumulus clouds look like pieces of cotton wool with rounded tops and often with flat bases. They are a fairly low

24

cloud but towering cumulus can extend perhaps to 10,000 feet amsl. In general they portend fine weather, except when they persist until evening, which is a sign of rain.

Stratus, as the name suggests, is a layer cloud and can extend from surface level as fog up to about 6,500 feet or more amsl. Alto-stratus can have tops over 20,000 feet. A further type of cloud is cumulo-nimbus which is associated with cold fronts and thunder-storms. These clouds can extend from a base of approximately 5,000 feet to tops of over 40,000 feet amsl. They usually appear white at the top, turning to grey or even coppery colour in between, and black at the base. Sometimes cumulo-nimbus clouds spread out at the tops producing a shape like a blacksmith's anvil. Cumulus cloud in daytime usually brings fair weather, and strato-cumulus (layered cumulus), showers. Low stratus and alto-stratus (high stratus) can bring much rain.

A few more sayings based upon folklore

(a) When the sun rises through dispersing stratus it suggests a fine day.

(a) When the sun rises on a cloudless horizon the weather will be settled for about twenty-four hours.

(c) A grey sky in the morning suggests fine weather.

(d) A grey sky in the evening portends bad weather.

(e) 'Red sky at night, shepherds' delight.' Fine weather for about twenty-four hours. 'Red sky in the morning, shep-herds' warning.' When the sun rises through a bank of cloud which persists, it portends unsettled weather for about twenty-four hours.

(f) A bright yellow sunset portends wind.

(g) A pale yellow sunset portends rain.

(h) Dark patches of cumulus cloud portend rain.

(i) When the air is dull and heavy and cloud persists over hill tops, it portends thundery unsettled weather.

(j) Soft delicate clouds suggest fine weather and a moderate breeze.

(k) Clouds with rough, broken edges bring rain and wind, but clouds with clear-cut edges suggest a clear sky later.

In attempting to forecast weather by cloud formations, it must be borne in mind that local geographical features, such as mountains, hills, coastlines, large lochs and reservoirs and also river valleys, do modify general weather considerations. Local opinions are, of course, always worth studying.

Apart from their usefulness in providing approximate short term weather forecasts, clouds are most important to game fishermen. They diffuse and break up the sunlight, thus rendering the line and leader less conspicuous against the background of the sky within the field of vision of the fish. To present the necessary illusion, it is usually accepted that a bright fly is best on a bright day and a dull fly on a dull day, but it has been known for the converse to be upheld, particularly having regard to baits used early in the season for salmon spinning. The brightness or dullness at any time will, of course, depend upon the amount of cloud cover and upon the time of the day. Other conditions being suitable, good sport can be had when the light is continually changing, as clouds pass over the sun. Light is in these circumstances reflected by the gold or silver in the body of the artificial and can attract the attention of the fish.

Layers of cloud also affect the rate of surface cooling of the land and water (terrestrial radiation). The rapid cooling of the water surface after sunset will not be so pronounced with cloud cover since the clouds themselves reflect back to the earth its earlier radiation. With little or no wind these can be ideal conditions for a hatch of natural flies to continue after sunset and indeed after darkness, particularly with buzzer *(Diptera)* and sedge or caddis *(Trichoptera)* on rivers, lakes and reservoirs.

Fog and mist

The meteorological definition of fog is visibility in precipitation of less than 1000 metres, whereas mist is similar but with a visibility of 1000 metres or more, so that mist is really thin fog. Both fog and mist can be more loosely defined as low stratus cloud and is formed in the same manner as higher cloud and other types of precipitation by the cooling of moist air to below its dewpoint temperature (100% relative humidity). The condensed water droplets form around particles of dust in the atmosphere, and in the extreme caused one-time London smog.

Fog and mist are of some importance to the fisherman because their presence on water indicates that the water temperature is higher than that of the air. The chilling of the water surface will most certainly put the fish down. The formation of radiation fog is a good example. Fog on large open waters can also cause problems for the fisherman, who unless he knows his bearings very well, could be in jeopardy on a rocky shore, apart from the indignity (as in flying) of just being lost. A wise fisherman will always carry a small pocket compass in his kit, in addition to a torch which he will need at dusk.

How to find true north with a watch from the position of the sun.

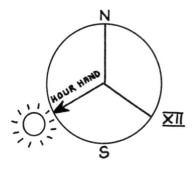

If in a low mist the silhouette of the sun can be observed, the direction of south (or its reciprocal north) can easily be ascertained with the aid of an accurate watch (not the digital variety). Point the hour hand towards the sun. Bisect the angle between that and XII o'clock and the bisection line will be the true south/north axis. From the sun's position, it should not be too difficult to find out which direction is north and which is south. An allowance should of course, be made to take account of British Summer Time, when applicable.

When fishing for salmon in conditions of low cloud, fog or mist, the ghillies say that 'when the mist (scotch mist?!) covers the ben (the top of the mountain), the salmon or sea trout will not take'. A little thought would suggest a tendency to a low barometer in these circumstances. Therefore, all other factors being the same, one would expect a lower water oxygen content and a consequently low metabolism of the fish, and limited activity and alertness on their part.

Haze

This weather phenomenon, caused by the concentration of dust particles, usually in dry or unsaturated air, is evidenced by poor visibility occurring particularly during periods when the barometric pressure is high and is affectionately termed by meteorologists 'anti-cyclonic gloom'.

Haze differs from mist in that little or no condensed water vapour is present in the former.

Game fish do not appear too happy in hazy weather, as in misty weather 'when the ben is capped'. This is not necessarily because of the haze in itself, but because of the conditions which give rise to the formation of haze – high barometer possibly causing an excessive availability in the oxygen content in the water at such times – which make the fish heady and lacking in mental alertness. A change in conditions is needed, such as a moderate but rapid reduction in barometric pressure, and the haze will then lift and the oxygen content of the water will become normal, and awaken the fish from their lethargy.

Precipitation

Precipitation occurs when moist air is cooled to its dewpoint temperature and becomes saturated (100% relative humidity), such as when a warm moist wind from the south-west strikes the mountain areas to the west of these islands and is forced up into cooler regions and condenses.

Precipitation can take the form of rain, snow, dew or hoar-frost. In itself it does not necessarily affect the taking or feeding habits of game fish. It is only the conditions which cause the precipitation that are really relevant.

Rain is usually associated with both a falling barometer and thermometer. The reduced atmospheric pressure will, of course, give rise to a lower dissolved oxygen content in the water, but the lower air temperature may marginally cool the water surface and put the fish down. On a first consideration, therefore, rain may seem not to be very good for the fishing. On the other hand, rain can bring the fish on the feed, because insects in the air are often brought down on to the water and because rain, heavy rain, particularly, breaks up the surface of the water and its oxygen content is marginally increased.

Rain, too, can be associated with a soft moist airstream from the west or south-west, especially if it is light and continuous, but this does not always apply.

How much these various weather factors together affect the fishing, one way or the other, really depends upon the degree of change: that is, the extent of the reduced barometric pressure and temperature, the heaviness of the rainfall and the amount of natural fly in the air at the time. Any sort of change in conditions can, therefore, be sufficient to shake the fish out of their inactivity and bring them on the take in the case of the salmon and on the feed in the trout's case. In any case, unless the fisherman himself is particularly well protected against the rain, it is he who usually suffers by way of a wet bottom!

Another folklore saying:

Rain before seven, clear-up before eleven:

At or about dawn the air is cool, and this coolness keeps the moist air at the clouds' altitude at its dewpoint temperature, and maintains the formation of the cloud. After sunrise, the air over the land progressively becomes warmer, as the land regions heat up, so burning off the cloud, and dispels the tendency to rain.

Snow is frozen rain and most of the effects rain has upon the fishing also apply to snow, depending upon the density of snow – one foot of loosely packed snow represents about one inch of rain. But it is the change in the various factors influencing the availability of oxygen to the fish which causes a change in their metabolic rate and therefore, in their mood physically and mentally.

Dew occurs at night and in the early morning, upon the rapid cooling of the earth's surface after a warm day with clear skies and high humidity, but with no wind; unlike the conditions which favour the formation of radiation fog, which in addition need a very light wind to act as a mixing agent.

Hoar-frost is frozen dew and occurs in conditions which favour the formation of dew, but at a surface temperature of 32°F (0°C) or below.

Incidentally, there is an old country saying:

After three days of hard frost (hoar-frost) there comes rain.

Thunderstorms, hail and icing conditions

In days of old, it seems that a popular misconception concerning the causes of thunder and lightning was that they were the result of two clouds coming into contact and banging together. We all know, now, that that is not true, although there is an element of truth in the saying. Thunderstorms are, in fact, caused by the meeting of two air masses, one cold and the other moist and warm, each having differences in static electrical potential or voltage. At some stage, the storm is triggered off, and the high voltage arcs across the atmosphere to the low voltage, and causes a huge spark or flash of lightning, which may be seen in the form of fork lightning or sheet lightning. The sound of the arcing is heard as thunder.

Both the lightning and the thunder occur instantaneously, of course, but, because light travels so much faster than sound, the clap of thunder is heard some seconds after the flash of lightning is seen, the time-lag depending upon the distance between the observer and the centre of the storm. The light/sound time-lag is about 5 seconds to the mile.

As the cold air pushes the warm air upwards into cooler regions above, cumulo-nimbus clouds are formed, giving rise to very powerful convection currents of air, causing severe turbulence which can turn an aeroplane on its back and possibly break it up. Pilots are therefore trained to avoid like the plague these 'cb clouds' as cumulo-nimbus are called. As the tops may be too high to fly over, and the bases too low to fly safely beneath, the alternatives are to fly round them or to turn back.

The mass of cold air, contributing to the cause of the storm, may contain what are called super-cooled water droplets, which are at freezing point or below and only freeze upon impact with other solids or liquids. For instance, if these droplets come into contact with an aeroplane, they freeze immediately and form rime (opaque) ice on the surface of the aeroplane, particularly on the wings. This results in increased weight, high stalling speed and in general a decreasing standard of performance. In these circumstances the pilot must ask Air Traffic Control for a change of altitude or flight level, which is below the freezing level. Modern de-icing equipment now prevents much of these problems. On the other hand, clear ice is formed, for example, in freezing fog when a vehicle passes through it.

Enough of this digression – *Hail* must now be considered. Super-cooled water droplets collide with other super-cooled water droplets and, as with an aeroplane, freeze upon impact, forming quite small pebbles of rime ice or hailstones. It is really a bad definition to refer to hail as freezing rain. These hailstones, very small at first, are carried up and down in the turbulent air by the convection currents. In the course of these rapid vertical movements, more super-cooled moisture becomes attached to the existing hailstones and freezes. Eventually, when the weight of the hailstones (known at times to be the size of golf balls) overcomes the force of the upward convection currents, they fall to the earth, sometimes causing much damage to roofs of buildings and greenhouses.

Taking a cross-section of a sizeable hailstone, one observes rings of ice, rather like the growth rings of a tree trunk, the number of ice rings denoting the number of up and down vertical movements achieved before falling eventually to earth. Each ice ring alternates between rime (opaque) and clear ice, the downward movements of the hailstones into cold air forming rime; and the upward movements (as if into freezing fog) (and into the warm air with resultant thawing) forming clear ice. In the warm mass of air, there must be some thawing of the outside coat of rime for clear ice to form.

Should, however, the cold mass of air not reach freezing point, there being no super-cooled water droplets as such, then the precipitation in the thunderstorm will fall, not as hail, but as heavy rain.

So much for the causes of thunderstorms and the associated hail or heavy rain.

Opinions seem to vary enormously regarding the effects of thunderstorms upon game fish. The writer has records to show that fishing, on occasions, has been very good before a storm. Then the air feels heavy and humid, the barometer is falling rapidly and the gusting wind is backing and a fair hatch of natural fly takes place for just a short while. It is really difficult to give any reason for the good result at a time when all weather factors seem to point to a lowering of the dissolved oxygen content of the water near the surface. It may be that the sudden downward trend in the barometric pressure has been sufficient, if only for a brief spell, to shake the fish out of their lethargy and bring them on the take.

On other occasions, the fishing has brought good results during a storm, when hailstones or heavy rain has been peppering the surface of the water, cooling it on the one hand and oxygenating it on the other. It may be that the increased availability of oxygen in the surface water is more beneficial to the metabolism of the fish than is the cooling effect detrimental and off-putting. As the metabolism increases, so does the activity and alertness which very likely brings the fish on the take or feed.

Towards the end of a storm, when it is starting to pass over, the wind begins to veer and increase in strength, pressure and temperature start to rise and relative humidity reduces (all good factors). In these conditions very good catches have been recorded. This is, of course, understandable, because a more stable situation is approaching, which should bring the fish on the take (that is if the actual storm itself did not shake them into activity).

During a storm countless natural flies are brought down on to the surface, and usually as it passes the trout start to mop up the drowned insecta in the more highly oxygenated surface water.

Differentiation has not, however, been made between the two main types of thunderstorm, because in general their causes are similar, being the association of cold with warm air and the vastly different static electrical potentials of the two volumes of air. Frontal thunderstorms occur mostly in spring and autumn and concern cold fronts and produce sheet lightning, whereas air mass thunderstorms are mainly restricted to the warmer summer months and are associated with fork lightning. Frontal systems are briefly considered in the next subsection of this chapter. Air masses were touched upon under Wind earlier, and as such are of little importance to fishermen.

Sheet lightning is reflected fork lightning.

Frontal systems

These are not all that important to the game fisherman as such, but as they have been mentioned earlier in the text it may be desirable to have them considered as a last section of this rather technical chapter on the element 'air', better perhaps described as 'weather'. Furthermore, the weather maps which are published daily in the national press and shown on television are studied, or otherwise referred to, by countless fishermen; so it is, perhaps, doubly relevant to make mention of frontal systems specifically, and to describe briefly the conditions which favour their formation.

Frontal systems can be most complex, but arise usually as a result of the meeting of a cold air mass with a warm air mass. The latter starts to climb up over the cold air, rises and forms a low pressure area from which the resulting fronts are formed.

The most usual form of frontal system is a warm sector depression (illustrated opposite), which can contain a warm front, a cold front and an occluded front (a combination of each), namely a warm front occlusion or a cold front occlusion. These are usually helpfully designated on the isobaric charts published by the media, but perhaps not quite so informatively on television weather maps. Perhaps it is that viewers of the weather news are considered more meteorologically enlightened than readers of certain sections of the national daily press! However, weather presentation has become much more comprehensive and informative since the use of satellite and the forecasts are indeed more accurate.

These little diagrams of the stages in the formation of a fully developed warm sector depression may help to explain the situation.

34

STAGES IN THE FORMATION OF A FULLY DEVELOPED WARM SECTOR DEPRESSION

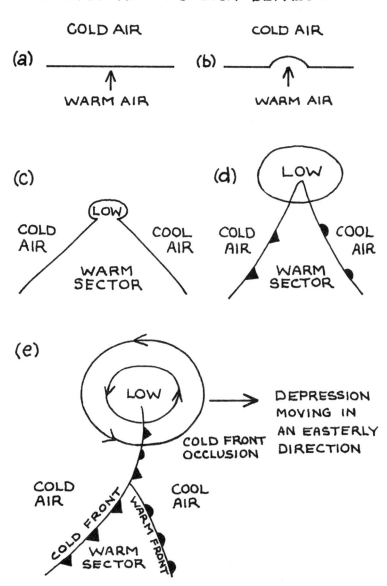

In diagram (e) on the previous page, the cold front is catching up on the warm front and forming an occlusion. It will also be noted that the air in advance of the warm front has become less cold, due to the advancing warm air.

Warm fronts are relatively slow moving, up to about 15–20 mph and, on average, approximately 200 miles in extent.

A falling barometer and the appearance of lightly packed cirro-cumulus cloud (mackerel sky) are usually the first practical warnings of the coming of a warm front. The cloud-base becomes lower as the front approaches and the cirro-cumulus gives way to alto-cumulus and then to alto-stratus cloud which brings continuous light to moderate rain and the wind backs and strengthens. At the arrival of the front, the cloud-base is right down to the deck (the surface) and the forward visibility becomes nil. As the front goes through, the wind starts to veer, the barometer rises, the visibility improves, the cloud-base rises, the rain abates and conditions usually return to those prevailing before the coming of the front, and the temperature rises.

The conditions during the approach of a warm front are usually sufficient to put the fish down and this situation can easily be recognised. With the passage of the front everything seems to improve (relative humidity less than 100%, rising barometer, rising temperature, veering softer wind) and the fish should then become more responsive.

Cold fronts on the other hand, move more rapidly, up to about 40 mph and extend no more, in general, than about 50 miles. Before the front the air is moist, warm and rather heavy, the cumulus cloud increases, giving way to towering cumulus and very often to cumulo-nimbus, the base of which becomes lower and blacker as the front gets closer. The wind will back suddenly, becomes very gusty in the unstable air, with moderate to very heavy rain and/or hail and sometimes thunder and lightning, as the front passes. The wind will then start to veer and moderate in strength, the cloud-base rises and the rain abates. The cumulus cloud begins to disperse

WARM FRONT ELEVATION

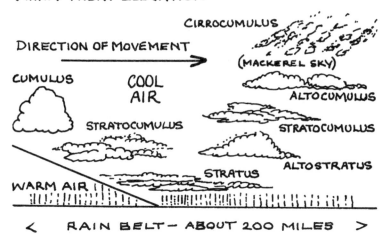

COLD FRONT ELEVATION

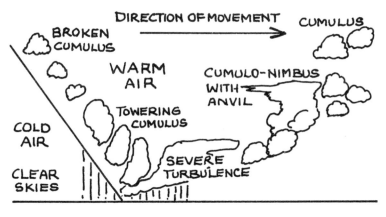

37

with bright periods until, in the case of a classic cold front, the sun shines from clear skies, but the temperature drops.

The approach, arrival and passing of a front will affect the fishing more or less in the same manner as during a storm and the various factors affecting oxygenation of the water and the bringing down of insecta upon the surface. If the fish became inactive and dour before the front, the rapid change in conditions after the front could shake the fish out of their lethargy into an active mood.

A trough of low pressure is another name for a weak cold front.

'The Earth is a solid, settled element; an element most universally beneficial both to man and beast.' Venator

The Compleat Angler
By Izaak Walton (1593 – 1683)

CHAPTER 3

EARTH, ROCKS
AND AN ALDER TREE

It became quite evident at a very early stage that it might be difficult to write anything informative affecting game fishing, under the heading of one of the elements, 'Earth'. After all, Earth is one of the first and principal elements of all, and without it there could be no Air or Water. Even the great 17th century angling bard and philosopher, Izaak Walton, did not exactly overstate the importance of the element, Earth.

It was only when some of the folklore and adages of the old-time Scottish ghillies were recalled for inclusion in the script under other elemental and weather headings that an idea began to germinate. It occurred to the writer that he had what he thought might be a suitable, although none too serious true story, to support the element, Earth, as affecting game fishing.

It is well known that, on occasions, when the salmon were dour and would not take, for whatever reasons, some ghillies, being mindful of their own reputations, as reflected in the success of their rod's angling art, would resort to one or more of a number of rather dubious practices of stoning, or otherwise disturbing salmon lies in the pools on their beat before their rod (master is not acceptable in this day and age) commenced to fish, with a view to awakening the salmon out of their inactive state in order to bring them into a taking mood. Whether this actually concerned the physical act of heaving into the water

39

large rocks, and making a huge splash, was not known, or whether it, perhaps less blamefully, concerned swimming a dog through the pool or, at best, spinning down the water in front of the fly rod, the writer was equally in the dark. So not having experienced any of these practices first hand, they were relegated in the mind to pure fantasy.

That was until March 1967, when I was fishing 'The Rising Sun' water at Umberleigh, on the Taw in Devon. Having taken two salmon of 10lb and 8lb from beat 10 on the Saturday, using a medium size copper Toby (the river was not then up to 'fly water', a temperature of 48°F (9°C) when a salmon's metabolism has increased sufficiently to render it active enough to take an artificial fly), I was well-pleased to take to a minor celebration with the locals in the bar that evening. It was really a little early for the Taw, but in that year, in March, the salmon had run up into the pools after considerable rain. On that Saturday, too, the water was fining down nicely. My records had shown the west-north-west wind had brought a mild airstream to the day and the air temperature rose considerably between 12 noon and 3 pm. The barometer had been rising a little and the water temperature had risen marginally by about 0.5°F. I had attributed my modest success to the water and weather conditions being right, and particularly to a higher oxygen content in the water as the day progressed into early afternoon.

Next day, on the Sunday, it was beat 2 for me, 'The Bear's Pit', as it was on alternate beats daily that guests were allocated to fish in rotation, No 10 being the lowest beat on 'The Rising Sun' water. Although it used to be a good pool, the very name 'The Bear's Pit' conjured up, in my mind, all sorts of forebodings and portents. My misgivings were, furthermore, heightened as a result of a previous evening's inspection of the beat and, particularly the pool. There, half submerged and lying right across the main salmon lie of this otherwise attractive pool, was a sizeable and bushy alder tree which, I was told afterwards, had been blown down in a March gale some days earlier. Not an optimistic fishing prospect, but I was determined to make the best of a bad job, despite the early morning weather forecast for the area being less than encouraging.

The experts predicted a backing wind to the north-north-west and eventually to the north-east in a day or two (in fact a nice drying wind – charming!). The day, they said, would be fine, mainly sunny later, but cooler. What could be worse? And the hotel barometer was falling. If I had access to a hygrometer (which I had not, then) the relative humidity would have shown a considerable fall later that day, to about 80%, I feel sure.

After a leisurely breakfast the next day, George Elsie, the proprietor of 'The Rising Sun', greeted me cordially and, after the usual and accepted pleasantries, requested some assistance 'for a short while' on beat 2 to try to shift the offending tree. Not that I had in any way complained about the tree being there at all, but quite naturally, I agreed to George's request without question. '11 o'clock then, Jack. My wife and I will join you at the river at 'The Bear's Pit' on beat 2 with ropes and hooks – and I know you have a strong pair of waders. I do hope we shall not upset your fishing too much and put the fish down.'

It did not occur to me then that I would have to do most of the work, because I was the only one who had waders. It all seemed such a good idea at the time.

At 11 o'clock on that Sunday morning and with the sun shining, George Elsie, all smiles, with his charming wife, appeared complete with all the tackle necessary to move the tree, which really was spoiling the pool. I had cast my Toby spinning bait in vain for the best part of an hour in the fairly limited area in the pool which was no more than 25 yards across from bank to bank.

'It really is good of you to sacrifice your time, Jack, to help us, because the fishing will be ruined for the rest of today after that bush has moved through the pool', the proprietor said to me.

Without much further ado I was cautiously entering at first the shallow water of the salmon pool, with a large steel hook or grappling iron attached to the end of a fairly thick rope in one hand, and a long stout wading stick in the other. It was not too difficult to reach the outside branches of the alder bush without the fairly fast-flowing river water getting in over the tops of the waders and, at that moment, I considered I was home and dry.

'Don't you think you ought to get the hook secured as near to the trunk of the tree as is possible?', shouted George, while his wife stood motionless some 20 yards away on the bank with him, holding the other end of the rope, which was more than long enough to do the job. 'I'll get as near as I can', I said. 'You can both start to pull when I give you the OK.'

I continued to advance still nearer to the main trunk and centre of the bush, which at the end of March had just started to break bud, so that the fairly thick trunk (of about six inches in diameter) could be seen through the bare branches. I was now upstream of the bush and I knew I could go no further into the deeper current without my waders being filled with water, but I managed to support my feet upon one of the fairly thick submerged branches, advanced into the tree and then reached out for the trunk. After two unsuccessful attempts, I got the large hook securely round the almost equally large alder trunk and breathed a sigh of relief.

'You OK?' shouted George, who had been standing still in a concerned manner for some minutes. 'OK, thanks', I shouted back.

George Elsie could see me in the water almost up to the top of my waders but could not appreciate, at that distance, that I was, in fact, standing on a branch of the tree and not actually on the river bed itself.

It was, of course, my intention, after securing the rope to the tree, to go back the way I had come to the safety of the shallow water, before assisting George and his wife with the pull on the rope to move the tree. So George accepted my affirmative re-assurance as the clue for both of them to start pulling on the rope.

'It will be quite easy, Jack', the proprietor had said initially, 'to pull the whole bush out into mid-stream and then let the force of the flow of the river take it away down-stream.'

That is exactly what happened, but with me caught in the middle of the tree. One hard but ill-timed pull by George and his wife from the river bank brought the tree out into mid-stream as planned, but with my weight on one of the lateral branches. The whole bush started to sink as it was being swept downstream through the cold deeper water, which by this time was well over the tops of my waders and now up to my chest, with me and the bush still sinking quite rapidly.

Had it not been for a shallow run of the river, about 30 yards downstream, where the tree eventually grounded, I would still have been hanging on and sinking with the tree. It would have been difficult to predict the final outcome!

Still holding on to the rope, George and his somewhat shocked wife moved fast to meet the dripping-wet, shivering figure of myself, whose only dry accoutrement was an ancient deer-stalker hat, and who was now hobbling heavily over the stones from the river with his waders full of cold water, 44°, to be precise.

'Sorry about that, Jack', said George, most apologetically, and apparently taking full responsibility for the resulting shambles. 'You poor man', retorted his wife, 'you must get back to the pub and have a hot bath'. 'And a large Scotch', I replied. 'I shall be quite all right.' 'You couldn't have left that blasted alder in a better place', said George, as he coiled up the rope and the three of us walked slowly back to 'The Rising Sun', I, in my wet, stockinged feet and soggy breeches, carrying my light cane spinning rod in one hand the dripping waders over my shoulder, supported by the other hand, and George's wife carrying my fishing bag and tailer.

It was still only 11.25 am, but it was a good fifteen minutes walk back to the pub. 'Great pity about your beat, today', apologised George again. 'I'm not finished yet', I replied, but I thought: he could have offered me an alternative beat. However he did not. 'Get some dry clothes on you', he said, as I slowly mounted the narrow staircase of this 18th century inn, and repaired to the bathroom.

It was exactly 12.15 pm when I got down to the olde worlde bar and looking a little more composed than when I had come in, I was told. There on the counter was a half-tumbler-full of scotch, and water to go with it, a mammoth size by any reckoning. But I was soon off back to the river bank with my rod and gear. I had only a few days and I wanted to make the best of them. This time I was in gum boots, in place of the drenched waders, so I could not go into the river too far this time.

George said he would come with me to make the alder tree secure to the bank, until the next flood. This he did in five minutes flat. As he started to walk back to his hotel the proprietor said in his deep voice, 'Good luck, Jack'. 'Thanks', I replied. 'I shall need it.'

I was most eager to fish 'The Bear's Pit', despite all the commotion which must have put down every salmon on that beat for some considerable distance, because it had the reputation of being a good holding pool. I cast a few times to get the hang of what was now a magnificent open pool. And to think that under an hour ago it was all so chaotic!

Hardly had George Elsie disappeared round the next bend of the river, when a fish took my copper Toby and I was into him. After 15 minutes, a beautiful fresh-run salmon with sea lice on him, lay played out, tailed and despatched on the short spring grass of the river bank. The salmon was an ounce under 12lb.

Needless to say, the movement of the blown-down alder tree through the stream had disturbed the pool and shaken the salmon into activity far more effectively than any rock-heaving by the most experienced of all Scottish ghillies.

I have, however, been left in some considerable doubt as to whether this chapter should have been entitled 'Earth' or perhaps 'Water', since I seem to have had my share of it both in the river and in the whisky.

The facts are as true as I can relate them after so many years.

CHAPTER 4

WATER

Constitution

Each molecule of the element, water, is made up of two atoms of the chemical element, hydrogen, and one atom of the chemical element, oxygen. Hence the formula, H_2O. That, of course, relates to pure or distilled water such as rain water. In reality, most water contains differing quantities of chemicals and salts, some harmful and some not, and also dissolved gases, such as nitrogen, making up the air which all animals, including fish, need in order to breathe, either through lungs or gills.

Pollution

Game fish will not survive long in water that is not clean and unpolluted, whether the cause of the pollution be organic or inorganic, dissolved or suspended. Sewage effluent and offensive chemicals not only make water unclean, but also destroy its dissolved oxygen, so vital to the survival of fish, and in the case of the trout, to the insecta upon which it feeds. Such a reprehensible state of affairs is in some instances called 'eutrophication' (despite the fact that 'eutrophic' – as opposed to 'oligotrophic' is the word used in a more general context to describe a natural water well provided with nutrients and

45

therefore an excellent habitat for fish – an example, perhaps, of the principle that one can have too much of even a good thing).

During the industrial revolution of the nineteenth century much of the best game fishing in the British Isles was destroyed. This was particularly so in the lower reaches of rivers through which migratory fish had to run to their spawning grounds. This was because of the effluent discharged by factories of the then new industries into those rivers which flowed through some of the larger towns and cities. And indeed, until quite recently no salmon had been reported in the Thames since the 1920s. It is, however, gratifying to learn that many of the one-time great salmon rivers, such as the Thames, the Clyde and the Tyne are now reporting runs of fish – in the case of the Tyne, quite a substantial one. This has been brought about not only through stricter legislation and more thorough enforcement, but also because of greater awareness and environmental consciousness on the part of the public at large, indeed ourselves.

It was not only in the large rivers that the degree of pollution was allowed to escalate, but also in some lakes, lochs and loughs and in not a few small trout streams. As an example one or two of Ireland's best known brown trout loughs have been affected adversely by effluent from concentrated pig farming. In that connection, it appears that although local authorities did, in fact, provide slurry tanks for the collection of this poisonous material to prevent its discharge into the waters of the loughs concerned, little or no provision was made for the emptying of the tanks and the harmless disposal of the slurry. Even where collections were made by some authorities, they were not established on a regular basis. The tragic result was that huge quantities of highly poisonous matter were discharged into some of southern Ireland's finest trout fishing waters, which many thousands of people, tourists and locals alike, sought for the enjoyment of their leisure activities. Even small factories in villages, market towns or in open country, cement works, timber mills and sugar beet factories, all took their toll of some

46

of the best trout fishing in local streams. It was not only industrialists who were to blame, but even not a few small farmers because of uncontrolled sheep dipping and the spraying of fertilizers and insecticides too lavishly on their land.

Thankfully, in recent years and for the various reasons already advanced, man has become more sympathetically inclined to the preservation of his fishing waters and other amenities – and long may this trend continue.

Alkalinity and acidity

Not all chemicals are, however, harmful to fishing waters. The presence of calcium dissolved in the water from limestone or chalk deposits (calcium carbonate – $CaCO_3$) raises what is called the pH value, which is a measure of the water's degree of alkalinity or acidity. Above pH7.6 water is said to be alkaline and below pH6.8, acid, so that neutral water has a pH value of about 7.2. As calcium content is essential to the growth of many creatures on which trout feed – crustacea in particular – a pH indicating modest alkalinity is good news for the angler.

Typical areas, where streams pass through lakes and reservoirs are situated on or near chalk or limestone, are Blagdon and Chew Valley lakes, both rain-fed from the Mendip hills in Somerset. There are also the chalk streams of southern England, the Test, Itchen, Avon and Kennet, to name a few, and fed by springs from the vast chalk deposits of Salisbury Plain and the Wiltshire and Hampshire Downs. In the English Midlands, we have the rivers of Derbyshire and Yorkshire, the Dove, Derwent, Wharf and Ure, which flow out of the Peak District limestone, whilst in Southern Ireland there are the midland limestone loughs of Sheelin, Ennal, Owel, and Deravaragh and further to the west on the borders of Counties Sligo and Roscommon, there is that magnificent piece of water, broken up by islands, Lough Arrow, which is fed by

47

underground springs from the limestone beneath it. Loughs Corrib, Mask and Conn are other fine Irish limestone loughs.

All these high pH value trout fishing waters provide weight-producing elements for the fish which feed upon the huge quantities of alkaline-bred insecta and wax fat and strong, to test the skills of the growing numbers of fly fishermen. All flora and fauna seem to do well in alkaline waters. From the 6.5lb brown trout to the most minute protozoa, the ecology of these waters is maintained in a good balance. So the trout feed on the fresh-water shrimp, louse and snail, upon up-winged duns and their spent spinners, sedge, beatles, boatmen and buzzers, as well as all sorts of nymph, pupae and larvae and all other insecta which hatch in or fall upon the water from the land. These various sometime water inhabitants in their turn feed and live on minute protozoa and other very small creatures, such as animal plankton, which in turn sustain themselves on algae and other microscopic specimens of plant plankton. These very small species of plant life thrive on the calcium and other dissolved salts and trace elements in the water in daylight, as well as on carbon dioxide (CO_2) exhaled by the fish, and on sunlight which provides the substance chlorophyl which gives all plant life its green colouring.

Water acquires its acidity for various reasons, but principally flowing through peat bogs and spagnum moss beds or through conifer forests which precipitate atmospheric acidity.

Acid water is not conducive to the growth of fish, plant or insect life to any extent, since it is a poor food producer. Salmon parr and trout which live in acid water are usually small and dark and the fly hatches are extremely limited. Fish will not, furthermore, spawn in *very* acid water because it kills the ova in the redds.

The low pH value waters are usually to be found in mountain-ous areas, such as the limestone-free areas of Scotland, Wales, and Devon; and in Ireland: Kerry, Connemara and Donegal. Some rivers such as the Liffey, on which Dublin stands, acquire their initial acidity from the mountainous or boggy areas where they rise and after flowing through or over limestone, the water becomes alkaline. There are certain water plants which thrive in acid water, such as peat plants, pondweed, wild ranunculus, milfoil, starwort, water celery and of course spagnum moss. Up-winged duns are not very plentiful in peaty or acid water, although the claret dun seems to thrive in it. The water leech and the water louse *(Ansellus aquaticus)* also do not seem to object to water with a low pH value.

The alkalinity or acidity can be tested with the use of litmus. Water with a high pH value will turn the litmus blue (alkaline) and that with a low pH value will turn the litmus red (acid).

Salmon return from the sea to spawn in the streams of their birth, wherever possible. It is, therefore, interesting to note that, in general, first-time spawners entering alkaline rivers to spawn tend to larger weights than those running up waters of an acid nature for the first time. The larger salmon have, of course, spent more summers in the sea than the smaller grilse of only one year in saltwater.

It is generally understood that a salmon running up from the sea can be a maiden fish or can have spawned in fresh water before; but, not so widely understood, a grilse is not only a fish up from the sea to spawn for the first time, but one that has spent only one summer in salt water.

And now to continue with the theory concerning relative weights or returning salmon to alkaline or acid streams to spawn. From scale readings taken from smolts on their way down to the sea, usually in May on the first flood, it can be shown that immature fish in the parr-to-smolt stage in acid waters spend longer in their nursery than do their counterparts in water of a high pH value. This is quite understandable because in low pH value waters there is, in general, a dearth of insecta to support the fish life and therefore the salmon parr are slower to grow to the smolt stage than those reared in alkaline water.

All this now leads to one interesting conclusion, namely that the age of a maiden fish, whether salmon or grilse, raised in acid or alkaline water, will be approximately the same from the eyed ova stage to the time the fish enters fresh water from the sea to spawn for the first time. It does, therefore, seem on average, that salmon reared in alkaline streams spend a longer period in the sea and achieve heavier weights on their return than do those reared in acid or peaty streams.

As an example, salmon from the Hampshire Avon run up to over 30lb and their average weight is very much higher than those from some Scottish rivers whose waters rise in the mountains, producing acid water. Here, the top weights are rarely over 15lb and the average nearer 8lb. The big Scottish rivers, such as the Tay, Spey and Tweed, which also produce large salmon, may be exceptions, or their head waters may tend to less acidity than many of the smaller Scottish rivers the writer has in mind, or perhaps run through alkaline soil where the parr grow quickly to the smolt stage, one cannot really be sure.

It cannot, however, be certain that this theory does in any way apply to sea trout.

Oxygen content and fish respiration

This subsection is to some extent a summary of the matters relating to oxygen included in previous sections.

Without a supply of dissolved oxygen in the water fish are unable to survive and with a deficiency, they become breathless, inactive and lacking in mental alertness. In these circumstances, the fish move into deeper water to preserve their energy, until conditions change.

Water obtains its oxygen from the air in varying conditions and by different methods:

(a) because aquatic plants (as in fact does all vegetation) give off oxygen in daylight and take in carbon dioxide (which animals and birds exhale). This process is called photosynthesis. At night, the process is reversed and decaying plants and vegetation use up oxygen in the water.

(b) when it is cooled (and water gives up oxygen when warm-ed), because cold water can hold more oxygen (some-thing under 9%) than can warm water (about 6%).

(c) when the barometric pressure is high (water gives up oxygen as the pressure falls).

(d) in the turbulent water under a weir.

(e) during a storm with heavy rain or hail.

(f) on a windy day when the water surface is broken up, particularly when 'white horses' appear.

(g) because alkaline water can hold more oxygen than can peaty or acid water.

A table of approximate water/oxygen content at various temp-eratures is set out below:

Water temperature	Cubic centimetres of oxygen per litre	
32°F (0°C)	8.3	
39°F (4°C)	9.0	highest content of oxygen possible when water is densest
42°F (6°C)	8.7	
48°F (9°C)	8.2	in this bracket trout feed well and
60°F (15°C)	7.0	will take a fly
68°F (20°C)	6.0	

With a lower oxygen content in warmer water, fish have to take in the same amount of oxygen to maintain their existing rate of metabolism, and therefore their rate of respiration has to be increased. The fish absorb oxygen as it passes through their gills and, to be able to survive comfortably, have to take in more water when it is warm than when it is cold.

Experiments have shown that a 10 inch brown trout increases its rate of respiration in warmer water:

Water temperature	Cubic centimetres per minute passing through the gills
42°F (6°C)	20
48°F (9°C)	28
60°F (16°C)	44

Water is capable of holding proportionately less oxygen (0.5% by volume) than is air (about 21%). As a result, a large quantity of water has to be taken in through the gills to extract a relatively small amount of oxygen. There is, however, some significance in the individual temperatures chosen in the above tables because, as considered elsewhere in the text, they all have regard to practicalities and fish behaviour at those temperatures. Cold water can hold more dissolved oxygen than warmer water. At 39°F (4°C) water is at its densest, and at that temperature contains the maximum amount of dissolved oxygen possible. As the water temperature rises (or indeed falls) less oxygen is capable of being held. At the increased temperature there is immediately more oxygen available for the fish's respiration. Excessive availability at low water temperatures, when the metabolic rate is slow, is not good. The effects on the salmon of oxygen content super-saturation and excessive availability at various water temperatures will be considered later.

Flow and level of water

In the middle of a stream the flow is faster and the water level higher than at the sides because of the friction of the banks. In some fast and very wide rivers, there can be a difference of some 6 feet in the height of the water in mid-stream compared with that along the banks. Here again, because of the friction of the river bed, the flow of water at the surface is faster than on the bottom. On a loch, or other area of open water, the waves made by the wind are longer and of a gentler slope in deep water, whereas they are shorter and steeper in the shallows. In boat fishing, this helps to locate the shallow water.

Density of water

Cold water is denser and therefore heavier than warm water which will rise to the surface. Water has its maximum density and weight and minimum volume at 39°F (4°C), at which temperature whether heated or cooled, it will expand. This irregular expansion of water explains why water in lakes starts to freeze at the surface and not at the bottom.

How water freezes

When the temperature of water falls below 39°F (4°C), so its density decreases and the colder water starts to rise to the surface. This convection continues until the surface water falls to 32°F (0°C), at which temperature it freezes and ice is formed on the surface. Shallow water will freeze before deeper water. In fast-flowing water, there is little difference between the temperature of the surface water and on the river bed. The formation of ice (and snow) forces out from the water all gases, including oxygen.

How water warms up

The rays of the sun warm the land directly by means of radiation. With water it is different, since no way can the heat of the sun be transmitted directly to heat the water. What happens is that the sun's rays penetrate the water and heat up the bottom which transfers its heat to the water by conduction. This warmer water being less dense and, therefore, lighter than the water above it, will rise to the surface by convection. These convection currents will continue until the whole volume of water is the same temperature. This, of course, is not achieved 100% in practice, because of surface evaporation and other cases of surface cooling. In these circumstances, the cooler and denser water will fall to the bottom and so the whole process of convection carries on, this time in reverse, as the lake starts to cool down slowly, and the sun's rays become less direct towards sunset. Here are a few more useful points to bear in mind:

(a) The colour of the bed of the stream or the lake is important. A dark colour will absorb the sun's heat rays better than a light colour. The same principle applies to the colour of one's clothes. Light coloured clothing feels cooler on hot days because it does not absorb so much of the sun's radiation.

(b) Shallow water will heat up and cool down sooner than deeper water because the greater the volume of water, the greater the specific heat involved.

(c) Water heats up and cools down much more slowly than does land.

Soft and hard water

Rainwater or distilled water is soft because it contains little or no dissolved calcium salts or trace elements. As the water starts to acquire these dissolved salts and gases, it becomes harder. The sea and other alkaline water is hard. Soft water, of course, when mixed with a given quantity of ordinary soap flakes will produce more suds and bubbles than will a similar volume of hard water.

Height and colour of water

A falling water level, or water at a static normal height is best for fishing, whereas rising water after a spate which has coloured the water, is not good, since, in a river, the indigenous fish, the brownies and the rainbows, go in under the banks or into deep pools to avoid the heavy water which contains much suspended matter; while the instincts of migratory fish impel them to resume movement upstream. However conditions just before a stream colours-up after heavy rain can be good enough to bring the fish on the take for a while as, of course, they can just as the water starts to fine down after it has ceased to rise.

Water temperature

Much on this subject was included in the section on air temperature because it was felt that a consideration of air temperature was pointless unless associated with its effect upon water temperature. A brief summary of the factors relating to water temperature and their effect on game fish behaviour will not now be out of place:

(a) Water acquires its heat indirectly from the sun.

(b) Water temperature is further modified by the effects of evaporation and wind.

(c) There are small short-term or diurnal variations and larger long-term or seasonal variations (see separate subsection at the end of this chapter on summer and winter stillwater temperature variations).

(d) Fish, being cold blooded, acquire their body temperature from the water, and their blood temperature in turn directly controls their rate of metabolism, which consequently controls their respiration.

(e) At or below a water temperature of 39°F (4°C) the metabolic rate of the fish is low and consequently they lie dour in deep water or in slack water away from the main stream and both their physical and mental capabilities are inert. This can be likened to a sort of short-term hibernation.

(f) As the water temperature rises in the spring of the year, at 42°F (6°C) and above a salmon will have increased its rate of metabolism sufficiently to run up over a weir from the white water, but between that temperature and 48°F (9°C) will not move far to intercept a bait, let alone an artificial fly.

(g) At 48°F (9°C), the minimum fly water temperature, a salmon will move to take a fly.

(h) Trout will similarly seek to increase their food intake, as the water temperature rises and their metabolism is increased.

(i) A rise in water temperature also increases the activity of natural insecta.

(j) The water temperature of rivers, depending upon the rate of flow and the elevation of their sources, does not, in general, rise much above about 60°F (16°C) but, of course, there are exceptions.

(k) In still waters it is different. Brown trout feed well and survive best between 48°F (6°C) and 60°F (16°C).

(l) Rainbow trout, however, do not like very cold water and feed best above about 60°F (16°C) and up to about 77°F (21°C).

(m) Water temperature is the most influential of all the elemental determinants of game fish behaviour.

(n) water temperature controls the rate of metabolism and respiration, no doubt, but it is the availability of dissolved oxygen which greatly determines whether a salmon will take or not.

(o) Oxygen and its probable effects upon salmon taking-times is considered in a later chapter.

Seasonal variations in stillwater temperatures:

Summer (July)	water layer
up to about 60°F (16°C)	epilimnium
46°F (8°C) to 60°F (16°C)	thermocline
45°F (8°C)	hypolimnium

Winter (January)	
32°F (0°C)	layer of ice
39°F (4°C)	hypolimnium

In a close winter, the epilimnium and thermocline become one with the hypolimnium.

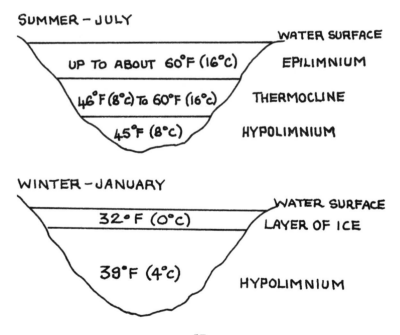

SUMMER – JULY

WATER SURFACE

UP TO ABOUT 60°F (16°C) — EPILIMNIUM

46°F (8°C) TO 60°F (16°C) — THERMOCLINE

45°F (8°C) — HYPOLIMNIUM

WINTER – JANUARY

WATER SURFACE

32°F (0°C) — LAYER OF ICE

39°F (4°C) — HYPOLIMNIUM

'Without the sun, nothing would be anything.'

Anon.

CHAPTER 5

FIRE

Sun

Light

This great and wonderful luminary of nature transmits heat and light to the earth by means of solar radiation. The effects of this are greater or less, all other elemental conditions being the same, according to the time of the day (diurnal) the season of the year (seasonal).

Light will *enter* water at any angle between 0° and 90° (though much will be reflected at glancing angles). However light cannot leave the water at angles greater than 48°. A light-coloured bottom will reflect more light than a dark-coloured one.

When the surface is broken up by wind or waterfall, the light rays become refracted (broken up or bent) at the surface and their powers of penetration become less. The underwater light becomes subdued and the underwater image in the fish's vision is just about normal and this is beneficial for the fishing. In strong sunlight and with little or no wind, the fish can be dazzled by strong direct rays (or almost direct rays, because there is always some refraction of light through water). These conditions are not good. On a dull day with some wind, diffused light does not penetrate well and this can also be favourable for the fishing.

In water which is not clean or in which suspended matter, such as algae, exist, the underwater vision is further restricted.

Vision of the fish

The deeper a fish lies in the water, the greater its cone of vision, but it is unable to see objects above surface less than an angle of about 42° with the horizontal. This cone is aptly named the fish's window.

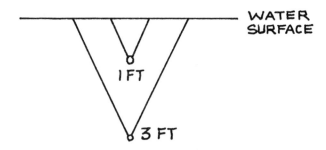

A fish can see objects more clearly against a dark background, such as the river bank, than against the sky, the light of which can dazzle it. Images at bank level, however, are only usually observed in the peripheral vision. It is always good fishing practice to keep one's own silhouette below a sky line and to get as near to ground level as possible to cast, when one's hopefully-camouflaged appearance should blend into the background. In that connection, for river fishing at any rate, drab brown and green clothing is to be preferred and in the case of boat fishing, blue or off-white is acceptable (so, not too much Persil, please, when washing fishing shirts!).

Whilst on the subject, never put a shadow on the water when the sun is behind the rod. It is better to cross to the opposite bank, even though one's own vision of underwater objects will not be so good. Casting a shadow on the water really is one of the seven deadly sins of fishing (see Appendix 1) and, in terms of degree, can be as detrimental to good sport as stamping about on the river bank. Mind you, the great Piscator would not have liked any of it and the writer quotes again from Izaak Walton's *The Compleat Angler:*

'and be quiet and go a angling. . . study to be quiet'.

Enough of digression – we must press on.

In the fish's cone of vision there is, of course, mainly sky, but images on the bank can be observed less acuitively in the periphery, but more so the deeper the fish lies.

Fish possess only panoramic and monocular vision and are unable to focus both eyes or judge distances too accurately, unlike man who has binocular vision. That is why fish will take short on occasions, because of dazzling or other light conditions.

It must be remembered that fish cannot move their eyes or their heads to avoid light, neither do they possess eyelids or eyelashes, which can be closed to protect the sight against the direct rays of the sun. Furthermore, fish are unable to contract or dilate the size of the cornea of the eyes, as most animals can do, to restrict the amount of direct light striking the retina. Because of the panoramic vision, movement of the object is most important and an object is judged by the size, shape and the amount of light it reflects.

The amount of light penetrating the water, depending on cloud cover, will affect the depth at which fish will be lying. On bright cloudless days, the fish, finding the direct rays of the sun troublesome, will be lying, and perhaps feeding in deep water. On duller days, when there is cloud cover, but according to the season of the year, of course, the fish will take up positions in fairly shallow water, near a ledge or shoal, resting their bellies upon a flat rock, ready to be able to take refuge in the nearby deep water when danger approaches.

In stillwater, fish usually move into wind or lie near the surface, or in midwater heading into wind, depending upon conditions, but when the wind is blowing out of the sun, as it were, then the fish will be dazzled by the glare of the direct rays. In these circumstances it will be difficult for the fish to see an artificial fly clearly, if at all.

Then, when fishing in a boat with the wind blowing out of the sun, it would perhaps be better to beach the boat, secure it and fish from the bank, maybe from a point or promontory, and cast across the wind.

In addition, it is advisable to avoid standing up in a boat, for fear of the fish observing your movements and being spooked by them. In any case, particularly in a strong wind, this practice can be particularly dangerous for the occupants of the boat.

In its cone of vision a fish sees its surface food as a silhouette blurred against the sky. Outside the cone, surface food is seen against the reflection of the bottom on the undersurface of the water, with, perhaps, only pieces of the flies' hackle showing through.

In its cone of vision the fish sees underwater-food somewhat blurred and indistinct. Outside the cone, underwater-food is seen at quite a distance against the reflection of the bottom on the undersurface of the water.

The area of the cone is enlarged by refracted light entering it from objects outside and above the area. A fisherman at a distance of about 30 feet from the fish is sufficiently inconspicuous, provided he is not placed more than 5 feet above water level. If he is closer or higher, his image will appear to the fish on the periphery of its vision.

Fish are unable to see anything behind them within a cone of 60° around their longitudinal axes. When fishing or just observing, and so as not to spook the fish, or otherwise put them down, it is usually better to cast and approach upstream, depending upon the wind and the rod's position in relation to the sun.

With regard to a rod's varnish finish, fish are known to have been spooked by the flash of a rod as sunlight is reflected from its glossed surface. A new rod, particularly one of built cane, should therefore be finished in flat varnish, which should also be used when completing a renovation job. Carbon fibre rods finished in mat black, are best, no doubt, in that respect.

An underwater flash of light is, however, attractive to the fish, when it is reflected off a bright part of a bait or glossy hackle, or the gold or silver body or ribbing of a fly; but a bright, hard, glaring light is never conducive to good sport.

Rainbows and how they are formed

The weather phenomenon (and not the fish!) is the subject for discussion under this heading. They are formed during rain showers, and the sun's rays are reflected by the raindrops to form a solar spectrum, the colours being red, orange, yellow, green, blue, indigo and violet. In heavy rain, the colours are more vivid than in light rain. To form a perfect bow, the sun must be fairly low in the sky, that is during the morning or evening, since a rainbow cannot be formed when the sun's azimuth is more than 42°. (The same limitation as for a fish's above-surface vision).

A rainbow in the morning usually portends wet weather since the sun, shining from an easterly direction, reflects the bow on to the clouds in the west, whence the wet weather comes. A rainbow in the evening usually portends fine weather the next day.

Sunrise and sunset

When it was intimated earlier in this subsection that the sun comes up from an easterly direction, the vagueness was deliberate. The sun does not, of course, always rise from due east and set in the west but only at the spring and autumn equinox around the end of March and September respectively, when the hours of daylight and darkness are the same length, namely 12 hours each. At the two extremes, round about midsummer's day in June, the sun rises nearer to the north east and sets towards the north west, whereas at Christmas time, the rise and set is nearer the south east and south west, respectively.

Moon and the solunar theory

It is well known that the moon and its phases have a direct effect upon the tides of the seas and oceans (and also upon some of us humans!). It has, also, long been established that this satellite affects the behaviour and habits of fish and other animals at certain times during any one 28-day period of the moon's phase (a lunar period). Animals then become active generally, but particularly in their feeding habits, and at other times, less so.

The principle involved relates to the position of the moon in relation to the earth (its longitude) and to the sun (the time of day). The activity times, lasting for about one hour, are called 'solunar periods'. Maximum activity is said to take place at the time of the day when the moon is directly overhead, the fisherman's meridian of longitude (a major solunar period), or alternatively overhead the appropriate anti-meridian on the other side of the earth (a minor solunar period).

Tables have been prepared annually for some years by an American scientist, Richard Alden Knight. Although this gentleman died many years ago, the work of publishing the tables has been carried on by his wife. The tables are based upon the Greenwich meridian of longitude, 0°, and its anti-meridian, 180°. Adjustments must be made to the times given in the tables for places east or west of Greenwich, on the basis that 1° of longitude represents 4 minutes of time. An adjustment should also be made for local time, such as British Summer Time, as appropriate.

Having ascertained the times of the solunar periods from the tables, as adjusted, it would not be wise for them to be considered in complete isolation, because other elemental and weather influences can accentuate or modify the anticipated increase in the activity of the fish during the solunar periods. It is understood that the accuracy of the solunar theory has been tested in all parts of the world and in all conditions and Mr Knight maintained that fish do become more active and have feeding and taking times during the solunar periods. It could be perhaps that, if the times of fishing could be planned to coincide with the activity periods, much, otherwise wasted fishing time would be saved and the 'off' times used for observation, study and tackle preparation. From the writer's experience, there is a strong vein of truth in this theory. For other reasons, (mainly because of the amount of moonlight available at night), the particular phase of the moon at the time does affect the feeding and taking habits of fish. Trout, of course, do feed at night when the moon is full because of the increased activity of insecta at those times. Salmon will also take during the night of a full moon. However during the next day the activities of fish can be restricted. The best day-time fishing is said to take place during the first and last quarters of the moon, when the nights are dark, the fish cannot see too clearly to feed and are then perhaps less discriminatory in what they take.

For sea trout fishing at night, it is best if at all possible, to choose a dark still night, but one with a moon is not favourable. It is also essential to be very quiet.

A similar warning must be given about shadow on a moonlight night. As in the case of sunlight, always try to keep your shadow and that of your rod off the water, when the moon is behind you.

This applies even in the daytime, when the moon also appears to cast a shadow. If at all possible, try fishing across rather than down-moon. The best visibility is, however, obtained by fishing up-moon, as for down sun. When the moon first comes out, the fishing may appear to go off because the air seems to become cooler. The moon also has some effect upon clouds. A full moon, particularly, seems to disperse small cloud formations which are around when it rises.

Some folklore about the moon and the weather.

(a) If the weather is unsettled during the last two days of a waning moon, the weather will remain similarly unsettled for up to a week. If, however, settled weather persists during the last two days of an old moon, settled weather will be expected for some days.

(b) When there is a halo around the moon, rain will be expected and the larger the sooner.

Moon phases

are usually illustrated in diaries and in the press thus:

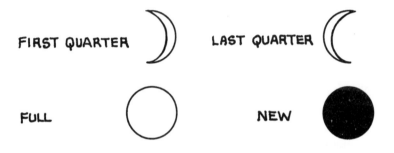

FIRST QUARTER   LAST QUARTER

FULL   NEW

CHAPTER 6

INTERMEDIATE CONCLUSIONS MAINLY AFFECTING TROUT AND THEIR FEED

The main elemental constituents affecting game fish behaviour have, perhaps, been considered in a fair amount of technical detail. A stage has now been reached when the effects of the two vital elemental factors, water temperature and oxygen must now be summarized: the former in this chapter, the latter in the next.

(a) *Water temperature* is vital because it directly affects the fish's rate of metabolism and therefore its propensity to be active or lethargic, and consequently to take or not, as the case may be.

(b) Water warms up and cools down much more slowly than does land, and water temperature is not only affected by the sun's radiation, diurnally and seasonally, but also by other air factors and weather conditions, mainly air temperature, wind, relative humidity and cloud cover.

(c) It is not just one factor alone which affects water temperature but a combination of all of them, some tending to increase and others to decrease water temperature.

(d) The rays of the sun indirectly and slowly heat up, during the hours of daylight, the water, which cools down during the period of darkness.

(e) As the sun gets higher in the sky, as spring gives way to summer, so the heating up of the water becomes more effectual as the hours of daylight are extended.

(f) *Air temperature* is indirectly affected by solar radiation, but the cooling of the surface of the water, substantially during the hours of darkness, which increase in length as autumn goes into winter, has the greatest effect upon water temperature.

(g) *Wind,* depending upon its air mass source, has a similar effect to that of air temperature in its ability to cool down or warm up a water surface.

(h) *Relative humidity.* This will, also, depend upon the source of the airflow and it must not be overlooked that a dry, none-too-cold wind from, say, the south or south east, will tend to evaporate and therefore to cool the surface of the water, even when the sun is shining from a clear sky and tending to warm up the water marginally during the daytime.

(i) *Cloud cover* has the effect of reducing, towards dusk, terrestrial radiation or the cooling of the earth's surface into space, by reflecting the escaping heat back to the earth and thus preventing the, otherwise, diurnal cooling of the water surface.

The general message is that one elemental or weather factor alone and in isolation cannot affect game fish behaviour. So it is therefore a question of elemental pluses and minuses, as to whether the water surface warms up or not, or does indeed cool down. If it does warm up, the warmer water being less dense than the cooler water below, remains on the surface and the fish tend to move higher up in the water or into the shallows.

Similar conditions also cause insecta to become active enough near the surface to bring the trout on the feed.

On the other hand, when, on balance, the various factors affecting water temperature do, in fact, cool the water surface, then the cooler water, being more dense than warmer water, will start to fall towards the bottom, underneath the warmer water. In this manner, convection currents are set up. These vibrations are detected by the fish in the sensitivity of their lateral lines and to avoid the considerable discomfort caused, they retire to deeper water, the temperature of which is more constant.

To sum up very briefly, therefore, but not to over-simplify the position, the ideal set of conditions to bring trout on the feed (but not necessarily to inspire salmon to take) appears to be: Adequate cloud cover of high stratus or alto-stratus, with the air temperature higher than that of the water and a mild south-westerly flow of moist but not saturated air (and, therefore, no precipitation).

Against that, the worst possible conditions for gamefishing might be: Clear skies with bright sunshine and a dry gusty wind from the north east of force 3 to 4, with glare from, and a scud on, the water; or the wind blowing out of the sun in equally squally conditions. Should the wind drop in the evening, rapid earth cooling would ensure that the air would be cooler than the water. What could be worse?

The two extremes have been given, but more often than not, conditions vary between the best and worst. With a little knowledge and experience, one should be able to detect a pending improvement in some of the elemental factors and be prepared for a period of better sport.

Examples might be the approach of the 'witching hour', usually accepted to be between 12 noon and 1pm (when, all other conditions being equal, the air and the water temperatures should have increased – the water temperature perhaps only marginally) or the veering of the wind from, say, the south-east to south or south-west, the increase in cloud cover or the reduction in the wind strength (but not necessarily to flat calm), to mention just a few favourable trends.

A veering wind has been mentioned and this presupposes a rise in the barometric pressure, not a factor really affecting water temperature, and if so only indirectly, but 'oxygen effects on the salmon' will be considered fully in the next chapter.

CHAPTER 7

OXYGEN – POSSIBLE AND PROBABLE EFFECTS ON SALMON

So far, the effects of the elements on the fish, and, therefore, upon the fishing, has related to the weather elements – air, water and sun. It has been shown that there are different factors affecting water temperature which increase or decrease the metabolic rate of the fish. This helps to control the amount of energy necessary for its normal activity. However, water temperature can not be considered in isolation, but must be taken in conjunction with oxygen, the water content of which has been discussed earlier.

The quantity of dissolved oxygen in the water is vital for the fish's survival and comfort. The fish can control its intake of oxygen by regulating its respiration, depending, of course, upon the existing rate of metabolism and the necessity, in the case of migratory fish, to conserve its energy for the remainder of the arduous journey it will soon have to make to the spawning grounds, possibly in mountain streams.

In this connection, it must be borne in mind that it has been scientifically established that salmon not only do not, but cannot, feed in freshwater. Even if they were so inclined, the digestive organs would not be adequate to perform their proper function. The only instinct, after self preservation, is to get to the redds to spawn as expeditiously as the conditions will allow. For this purpose, salmon need varying amounts of energy and therefore available dissolved oxygen from the water, depending upon the flow of the stream and the obstacles to be overcome.

To summarize those factors already considered in detail, the content of dissolved oxygen in the water is maintained by a number of biological and meteorological factors. These are aquatic plants increasing barometric pressure, wind and other surface water disturbances, and lastly – and most important of all – water temperature.

It is, perhaps, paradoxical that increases in water temperature up to about 60°F (16°C) have the effect of advancing the metabolic rate, whereas they also reduce the amount of dissolved oxygen which the water is capable of holding at that temperature. This causes some super-saturation of oxygen in the water. Perhaps it is this additional availability which gives the salmon the extra energy for its often short-period bursts of mental alertness and physical activity?

Adequate supply infers that there is sufficient dissolved oxygen in the water for the fish to regulate the respiration, to maintain the necessary rate of metabolism having regard to the strength of the current, which mainly controls its energy requirements.

The salmon is able to make all the necessry adjustments to its rates of respiration and metabolism to provide sufficient energy to jump a weir with water temperature at no less than 42°F (6°C) and to take a bait at quite close proximity, at that water temperature or more, or to take an artificial fly at no less than 48°F (9°C). At very low water temperatures the fish will regulate its oxygen intake to the somewhat low-energy requirements for the time being.

Inadequate supply (*Anoxia*) will produce breathlessness and a higher rate of respiration. The fish will be lacking in both mental alertness and physical activity. In these circumstances, which could be caused by very high water temperatures or some degree of eutrophication as a result of pollution, the fish would most probably go into deeper water, where the oxygen content might be greater and where the energy requirement would be much less for the fish to maintain its station.

71

Super-saturation is caused, in general, when the temperature of already oxygen-saturated water is increased, thereby reducing the amount of dissolved oxygen capable of being held in the water at the increased temperature. This gives rise to some super-saturation, thus making more oxygen available to the fish.

Excess availability really means what it says – too much oxygen. In these circumstances the salmon become heady, over-enthused and suffer a loss of mental alertness. This, perhaps, can be likened to a human being having had one or two 'over the eight' and suffering from an excess availability (and intake of alcohol which has, perhaps, too readily been taken up). In no way, however, does it seem that the physical activity of the salmon will be affected by an excess availability of oxygen. Nevertheless, in these circumstances the fish will escape to deeper water where they will lie lethargic and dour until conditions change. In particular what is needed is a drop in the water temperature, if only slightly, to increase the oxygen holding capability of the water and to reduce or eliminate the excess availability.

What does make a salmon take?

This matter was briefly considered earlier in the text and most salmon anglers subscribe to the view that reflex action, (or simply habit), frustration, aggression or even inquisitiveness are at times responsible for the salmon suddenly coming on the take and then perhaps, after a short period going off as quickly as they came on.

But why do they come on the take when they do?

The whole subject is the $64,000 question, and various theories have been put forward over the years since time began. Some writers have likened the problem to a maze or a nightmare, others to a jigsaw puzzle with possibly some pieces missing, others to other apparently insoluble problems. But, if all the exits were known, all the enigmas of the subconscious mind reconcilable with truth, and all the pieces of the puzzle available, game fishing with its inconsistencies, apparent irreg-ularities and this seeming fickleness of the salmon, could not possess the same charm or retain the same interest.

During a period of enforced vacation during the summer of 1970 in the Scottish Highlands, like many other fishermen interested in meteorology, the writer kept daily records of the variable weather factors considered in the text. He did in fact record trends of air and water temperature, barometric press-ure, relative humidity, approximate wind-speed and direction, cloud cover, general weather and height and colour of the water for each of the fishing sorties, and more particularly at the time of each take.

It was somewhat confusing, at first, because it seemed that fish were caught not only on the days, or during the periods when the elements seemed right (and sometimes not even upon those 'good' days at all), but at other times, when one or more of the elemental factors were definitely unfavourable. In the end, concentration was given to what appeared then to be the main controlling factor – *water temperature*. From that time, both the successes and the failures did, in some way, conform to a sort of taking pattern.

Whilst the importance of oxygen was considered to be of no little account and the elemental factors producing an increase or decrease in dissolved oxygen content were, of course, well known, the confusing point was that salmon did have taking times which certainly did not correspond on a day to day basis, or necessarily with the sometimes accepted good taking times of dawn, midday and dusk: and furthermore some of the taking times were of such a limited duration.

Neither of the advantageous elemental factors (producing an increase in water temperature, for instance) either singly or combined with others seemed to explain the various anomalous

73

situations which had arisen, and particularly what it was which contributed to the sudden mental alertness and physical activity of the salmon, sometimes only for short spells, during which it would take freely.

After much discussion with fellow anglers, ghillies and freshwater biologists and the reading of several books, the crux of the problem was narrowed down to a question of the availability of dissolved oxygen in the water and super-saturation of it caused by rising water temperature. This would make available extra oxygen for the salmon's blood stream, at a time when the rate of metabolism was fairly high, to give the required amount of energy necessary to boost its mental alertness and physical activity, if only for a short taking period. Even so the trend in the water temperature would have to be right.

Sufficient information now seems to be available for establishing, at least circumstantially, why salmon take when they do. The only way this can be done is to cite particular, and typical conditions during a day on a salmon water at various seasons of the year from March to October or spring through summer to autumn, having regard to the various and changeable weather conditions prevailing at the time, and as to their suitability for fishing.

For simplicity and easy reference, the information has been condensed and summarized on a record table. One day per month for each of six months at approximately six weekly intervals has been taken as having been typical for the time of the year.

Abbreviations used are explained at the foot of the table.

Observations on the recorded conditions

Early March This was the first fishing outing of the year and the picture in the forenoon did not look good. The temperature of the water was higher than that of the air. The barometer had been high for a few days, the relative humidity

was low with a drying wind and sunny with almost clear skies –
not a cheery fishing prospect on the Devonshire Taw.

However, after an early lunch, which was not hurried, conditions began to improve considerably. By 2.30pm the water
temperature was already 1°F higher. (An increase in temperature below 39°F does not cause a super-saturation of oxygen
in the water as it does when above that temperature, but on the
contrary some excess availability could occur). There is no
doubt, however, that the improving overhead conditions gave a
boost to the metabolism and put the fish into a responsive mood
which on this occasion brought the fish on the take. Indeed, the
barometer had started to fall, the relative humidity increased as
the wind backed and slackened to the north-west and the air
became more moist. The conditions were still fairly warm and
sunny but becoming more overcast all the time. The only fish
seen took a copper Toby as a sizeable cloud obscured the sun for
a short while – a dull bait on a fairly bright day.

It has been suggested, purely as an afterthought, that water
may be more susceptible to temperature rises below 39°F than
above it.

Mid-April   Here again on the Taw and the morning conditions were far from good, but at least the water temperature
was a little lower than that of the air. The barometer, however,
was low and the air was 100% humid in the light to moderate
continuous rain which began at dawn. 'Rain before seven –
clear up before eleven.' And that is about what happened.

By midday, the remains of the warm front was going through
and although still a little showery, the wind had veered and
freshened slightly, the relative humidity had started to fall and
the barometer was a little higher. All these favourably changing
conditions had been good for the salmon's metabolism, but it
was the sharp rise in the water temperature which must have
caused some super-saturation of oxygen in the water, possibly
to bring the salmon on the take.

With just one decent fish the writer was more than encouraged, because the elemental effects on the fishing, considered at

RECORDED CONDITIONS

MONTH	TIME	Wt.°F	At.°F	Bp.	Rh.	Cl.	W/V.	W.	TREND	RESULTS
EARLY-MARCH	10am 2pm	36 39	34 53	High St. to fall	87 93	0.10 0.30	NE4 NW2	Sunny Sunny	Not good Improving	- TT 1.30pm 1 S 14.5lb 2.5" copper Toby
MID-APRIL	9am 12 noon	42 44	44 52	Low St. to rise	100 97	1.00 0.80	W1 NW2	Rain Showery	Not good Improved	- TT 11.30am 1 S 12lb 2" B&S Devon
LATE-MAY	10am 1pm	50 52	51 59	Rising Steady	98 96	1.00 1.00	SW1 SW2	Overcast Overcast	Promising Good	- TT 11.30am-12.30pm 2 S 15.5lb-11.25lb Logie No. 10
	4pm 8pm	53 51	61 54	Steady Falling slowly	89 91	0.20 0.50	SE4 SSE1	Sunny Overcast bright periods	Deteriorating Improving	- TT 7.30pm 1 S 10lb S. tail No. 8
MID-JUNE	12 noon	55	65	St. to fall rapidly	95 rising	0.60	W3	Overcast bright periods	Not too good	-

RECORDED CONDITIONS continued

MONTH	TIME	Wt.°F	At.°F	Bp.	Rh.	Cl.	W/V.	W.	TREND	RESULTS
MID-JULY	4pm	57	68	Low	100	0.90	NW5 squall	Heavy rain	Poor	-
	5pm	58	59	Rising	90	-	NE3	Sunny	Improved then deteriorating	1 take S. tail No. 10
EARLY-SEPT	9am	54	50	high	100	-	Early L&V	Misty	Not good	-
	3pm	55	62	St. to fall	92	1.00	NNW2	Overcast	Improved	TT 1.30-2.30pm 3G 8.5, 8.25, 7.25lb Hairy Mary No. 8
LATE-OCT	12 noon	50	58	St. to rise	94 rising	0.70	SW1	Mainly overcast	Good	TT 11.30am 1S 12lb Hairy Mary No. 6
	4pm	50	58	Rising	97	0.50	W2	Bright Periods	Quite Good	2 takes S. tail No.8

ABBREVIATIONS

At.	Air temperature	Bp.	Barometric pressure
Cl.	Cloud	W/V	Wind Velocity
W.	Weather	TT	Taking Time
G.	Grilse	B&S	Blue and Silver
St.	Starting	°F	Degrees Fahrenheit
Wt.	Water temperature		
Rh.	Relative humidity		
L & V	Light and variable		
S.	Salmon		
S. tail	Stoats tail		

length in theory, were beginning to hold some substance in practice, particularly the effect of oxygen. On the whole it was a good fishing week with mostly rising water temperatures.

Late-May Travelling half way up Loch Shiel to where a sizeable river flows in, on this mild May morning, one could sense the bouquet of the Rhododendron and Azalea flowers as Holy Island was approached. From experience over the past few years, at that time, it meant that the mild airflow was coming from the south-west. A rough note of conditions had been made at about 10.00am before setting out. It was going to be a good day. The sky was, and had been overcast all night, so there had not been much earth cooling. The water temperature was well up for the time of the year, because most of May had been warmer than average and at noon on that day the air temperature was several points above that of the water. The main point was, of course, that the water, at above 48°F, was right for the fly and the floating line, and had been for some days. Because of the warm weather, there had been reports of early runs of spring salmon, since it is well known that the fishing on the Shiel in the Scottish Highlands does not really get underway until about the first week in June. The barometer had been rising and the relative humidity was high but not now at saturation point.

The fish must have been well on the take on our arrival, because within minutes a good fish took and was landed without problem in the large salmon net most always carried in the boat. A tailer is more convenient for the river bank. There is, perhaps, a further lesson here: the writer should have been on the water at least an hour earlier. Another nice fish was taken soon afterwards.

As regards the suitability for fishing on that May morning, on this occasion it will perhaps be best left to the reader to work out for himself just why the fish came on the take sometime between 10.30am and 11.30am. The only further indication that can be given is that the water temperature probably rose a point or two after the sun had got up.

Conditions started to worsen soon after 1.30pm and a lunch break was called for. By late afternoon, conditions had deteriorated considerably. Although the water temperature was a degree higher the barometer was now falling and the hygrometer showed a drop in humidity. A dryer wind was coming in from the south-east, as it backed and freshened. The sun was shining from an almost clear sky, and the day had become harder, after such a promising start. The salmon were probably lying dour and lethargic in deep water away from any current where demands upon its source of energy would have been greater.

After a good rest during the afternoon, sheltered from the cool wind and enjoying the warm sunshine in the beautiful but rugged countryside, fishing was resumed at about 5pm. It seemed that conditions had started to improve after the fairly weak ridge of high pressure had passed through. A third salmon was taken but it was not until afterwards that the weather trends were taken. The barometer had started to fall and the hygrometer was a little higher, the easterliness was going out of the wind and some cloud cover was returning. The really significant factor was, however, that the water temperature had dropped in the early evening, that is before the change in overhead conditions took effect. This cooling was no doubt caused by the drying wind (cool on this occasion also), which had evaporated and chilled the water surface, despite the warming effect of the sun's rays.

It will be interesting to consider the possible reason why the salmon did take when they did. To have two rather rapid water temperature changes within the day was, perhaps, unusual for the time of the year.

However, it does seem that the increasing water temperature in the morning did bring the fish on the take, probably because the availability of oxygen had increased to a point of slight super-saturation. Later, about lunch-time, the situation gave way to one of excess availability as the water temperature continued to rise. This no doubt, aided by the deteriorating weather conditions, put the fish down. Now this is the interesting point: the salmon did come on the take again after quite a large fall in temperature, which would, otherwise, reduce the rate of metabolism and contribute to the causes of the salmon's inactivity. Admittedly, the overhead conditions had started to improve, but only marginally. Even so, the possibility exists that the salmon did come on the take as a result of the excess availability of oxygen having given way to a situation of super-saturation, since the cooler water was able to hold more dissolved oxygen than when it was 2°F higher.

Altogether, this was perhaps one of the most interesting day's fishing of the whole trip.

Mid-July The month of July is usually good on the Shiel, but there are, of course, bad days. It is therefore interesting to show from the record, noted at the time, the adverse trends and how the elemental factors produced the unfavourable conditions. In that way changes for the better may be more easily recognised, and full advantage taken of, perhaps, only a short-period of salmon responsiveness.

On that day the conditions in the morning were not too good. Although the water temperature was higher than on the previous day, the barometer had started to fall rapidly, but the relative humidity had risen from an earlier low reading. The air temperature was increasing, the atmosphere was heavy and the salmon were dour. A storm was approaching and perhaps they were preparing to run on the higher water later, if not too coloured.

Fishing had to be discontinued for some minutes during the very heavy rain, but just after the cold front went through at something after 4pm, conditions did improve for a short while. The pressure started to rise and the humidity dropped. The squall had gone out of the wind which had veered to the north and the clouds were getting higher and clearing. The heaviness had lifted but the air was becoming cooler. If the salmon were shaken out of their activity at all by the rapid change to more favourable trends (which incidentally was fairly short-lived) the salmon did not show it and there were no takes.

By 5pm the air temperature had dropped considerably, although the water temperature had risen by a degree because of the warm heavy air which persisted all day before the storm. But now the sky was clear; the wind had veered further to the north-east and was dryer and much cooler. The glass was still rising slightly, but the hygrometer showed a sizeable reduction. The evaporation and cooling of the water surface had put the fish down, that is if there were any salmon left in the pools, but of course there would be others coming up to take their places had the original occupants run, and salmon do take when they are running. The water temperature was the key to the situation. It would have been higher but for the direct cooling effect of the cold, heavy rain produced as a result of the cold front.

In all these changeable conditions it is difficult to judge just how much the availability of oxygen in the water fluctuated during the afternoon. The rise in the water temperature after mid-day could have brought about some super-saturation of oxygen which might have encouraged some responsiveness from the salmon, but at that time, also, other elemental factors were pulling against the otherwise advantageous trend. As the cold front went through, conditions started to change again rapidly – for a time for the better; and to put the worst complexion upon the situation, the availability of oxygen, perhaps, was maintained in a super-saturation situation. But it is doubtful whether there could have been any excess availability. However the fish came short on the one take of the day after this short period of improved conditions. By 5pm the situation deteriorated again and the salmon, no doubt, were lying dour in deep water. They certainly did not like the dry north-east wind which was chilling the water surface.

Although no fish were landed, much was learnt from the changing conditions of the day.

Early-September Autumn had started to come upon us and the highland countryside looked magnificent. At that time of the year the fish can be expected to run almost at any time. There seemed to be quite a few grilse moving when conditions were favourable.

The situation on setting out was not good. The air was cooler than the water and there was still mist (radiation fog) which the early morning sunshine had intensified. The barometer was high and there was, of course, high humidity. The immediate prospects were not good, but they could only improve.

It was not until well into the afternoon that things got better. The glass started to fall from its high reading, the air was no longer saturated with moisture, and the wind had veered and freshened slightly. The conditions had improved and the day become softer. The really significant factor was that although the air temperature had risen quite considerably, the water temperature was now a degree higher. This, no doubt, put the fish into a responsive mood and brought on some activity, as the record shows.

Late-October   There would be fewer fresh fish running, and now would be a good time to get a not-too-stale fish just as conditions were changing. The conditions seemed perfect when the one nice salmon was landed.

Later, in the afternoon, although the air temperature was falling, both the barometer and hygrometer showed rises and the wind had veered and freshened. The fish came on about 4pm, but both salmon were lost on the take. They appeared to come short and misjudged the distance in the diffused light conditions which became quite dazzling in the bright periods. The use of the wrong pattern may have accounted for the afternoon's failure – a stoats tail can be very productive in bright conditions. Perhaps the size was wrong or a No. 8 Silver Grey would have done better. Still, it is not always good to job backwards, but making mistakes is all part of the learning process.

And an ingenious Spaniard says, that 'rivers and the inhabitants of the water element were made for wisemen to contemplate and fools to pass by without consideration'.

The First Day – *The Compleat Angler*
Izaak Walton (1593-1683)

CHAPTER 8

FINAL CONCLUSIONS

It is sincerely hoped that no game fisherman will ever become such an addict of weather trends that he will spend so much time reading his meteorological instruments as to have little time left to pursue his chosen craft and enjoy the study of wildlife activities, which are all part of the way of life that is fishing. In time, we can learn to judge the atmospheric changes without the use of instruments, the pocket thermometer, perhaps, excepted. It is, however, always helpful to be able to check up afterwards from the instruments themselves.

There is no doubt at all that of all the elemental factors considered as affecting game fishing, the two most vitally important ones are water temperature and oxygen content.

It has been shown that as the water gets warmer, so the metabolic rate of the fish increases, as does also the oxygen availability, the amount of it absorbed through the gills and, of course, the rate of respiration (depending upon the flow of the stream and energy requirements generally). At the same time conditions are usually right for insecta to hatch and the trout to feed. As is normal in all well-balanced waters aquatic plants keep up the supply of oxygen needed by both the natural fly and the fish.

Salmon, not feeding in freshwater, must, however, be affected by some influence which puts them into a mood responsive enough to take a bait or artificial fly, such influence being one

83

other than any of the elemental factors needed for the maintenance of metabolism alone. That influence is, no doubt, and can only be, the fluctuating availability of the dissolved oxygen content in the water.

It has also been shown from records that both a rise *and* a fall in water temperature can, in different conditions, bring the salmon on the take. These apparently conflicting statements, nevertheless, can be explained. It seems that no other elemental factors, either on their own, or combined, are able to satisfy both situations rather than the salmon's natural oxygen supply. As the oxygen-holding capability of the water reduces (as the water temperature rises) so the oxygen availability increases until a degree of super-saturation is reached and the salmon are stimulated to a greater alertness and physical activity and probably to a taking mood.

Should the water temperature carry on rising, that process will continue and a slight super-saturation will eventually give way to one of excess availability. At this point, the salmon become so enthused that they seem to lose their mental alertness and responsiveness and probably retire to slacker and/or deeper water. The physical stamina and activity does not, however, appear to be affected by oxygen excess.

When, later, the water becomes a little cooler, then any excess availability will give way again to a situation of super-saturation, when the salmon seem to revert to, or are shaken into, perhaps, a short taking period. Should the water continue to become cooler still and its oxygen holding capability increases, any super-saturation will be taken up by the water and the salmon will revert to, perhaps, a non-taking mood. It seems, therefore, without much doubt, that the oxygen supply provides the answers to the questions as to 'Why salmon take when they do?'

In connection with what prompts a salmon to take, whether naturally or artificially produced, it has been related how salmon can also be shaken out of an inactive state by water disturbances and this indeed has been proved to be so. But it nevertheless seems doubtful that a salmon will take a bait or an artificial fly outside of its normal taking times when elemental conditions and oxygen availability may not be favourable.

Over the years many theories and explanations, some well-reasoned and based upon records kept at the time, and other more speculative, have been advanced as to why salmon do take baits and flies and have definite taking times. Most devotees will agree that the effect of elements collectively plays a great part. It is, however, the theories on the fish's oxygen supply which have had the greatest impact. The writer must, therefore, take no credit at all for the originality of any such theories put forward, since he has merely wished to show that weather factors, conscientiously and regularly recorded at the time, have proved very much the same as others have proved in past years, but with a difference. The subject of the elements as affecting game fishing has been covered more or less, ab initio, with a view to instructing the beginner and perhaps interesting the more experienced game fisherman. The author will not, of course, have satisfied everybody, but that could not even have been attempted.

However, the reader should have a working knowledge of weather recognition and anticipation and if he is now able to differentiate, weatherwise, between favourable and unfavourable trends, he may, perhaps, save himself much futile and, therefore, wasted fishing time which could, otherwise, be devoted to water and wildlife study, or even to the reading of non-fiction effusions such as this, and with time to consider 'weather to fish', or indeed *whether* to fish or not.

CHAPTER 9

SOME MORE TALES
(but very little to do with the elements)

Coincidence

We must all at one time or another have experienced some sort of amazing coincidence, but I wonder whether there has even been one such as I am about to relate?

A few years ago I was fishing on Lough Currane at Waterville, Co Kerry, during the last week of September. Just prior to this visit there had been a few days of very bad weather with gale force winds followed by much rain. The lough was fairly high, and there had been a large late run of sea trout up the very short river of no more than half a mile in length from the sea. It was the fourth fishing day of my stay, just after a short sharp storm, with hail, had passed over. The barometer had started to rise and the air temperature had fallen a little. The wind had abated somewhat and veered, and the sky was beginning to clear. In fact a weak but classic cold front had just passed through.

I was using a floating line with an eight pound leader and three flies. I do not remember the particular patterns I had on the tail and the middle dropper but I well recall having on the top dropper an artificial daddy-long-legs, an imitation of the crane fly. There were no other boats where I had chosen to fish in the small bay at the top end of the lough, where the water flows in from the upper lakes. I had caught nothing all day. It was now about 4pm and I suppose I lost my concentration whilst I was sorting myself out after the short-lived storm. I must also have let my rod drop on the gunwale of the boat and although still holding the rod, I was, in effect hand lining. Then when I was least prepared for it there was a small take but I felt no more; but almost immediately, less than 15 yards away, a large sea trout leaped out of the water three times, quite obviously with one of my flies still in his mouth. There was nothing else to do but to wind in my line, which I did most forlornly, and to inspect the broken leader. Yes, he had taken the 'Daddy' all right, and the leader had broken at the blood knot, one of the weakest spots in any leader. Rather than bemoan my bad luck, or rather bad fishing, I proceeded to mount a new leader with, of course, a new 'Daddy' on the top dropper. But my run of bad luck, or bad fishing, whatever, had not ended. As I was tying on a small Raymonde on the tail (and I remember this well – size 10 it was) a gust of wind moved the rod, which was out over the gunwale, and took up the slack line and leader and tightened them *and* the hook of the Raymonde into the third finger of my left hand, right past the barb too. After securing the position of the rod across the thwarts of the boat I tried, in vain, to remove the unwelcome hook. All I did was of no avail, and had I continued with my amateurish efforts I would, no doubt, have done more harm than good. The finger was now gushing blood and the pain was acute.

At that moment I was able to recall the first and only other occasion when such an accident had occurred. It was in Scotland on Loch Shiel, and that time it was a size 12 Blue Bottle Spider. I remember 'wasting' several hours of good fishing time, taking the boat back to the mooring and driving all of five miles each way to the only Doctor available for miles around. I can see him now, a tall well-built, rather rugged but kindly Scot wearing a tartan kilt – yes, that's right, Dr Ian MacLoughlan was his name. In his calm professional manner, after my pleadings to save the fly, he stopped his examination and said:

'what is it you want saved, the finger or the fly?' Having been assured of the priorities, and after warning me that there would be some pain – a deft movement of his long artistic fingers, and the hook was out. Some pain, much blood, a word of appreciation and I was away with my fly back to the boat. That was some years ago and the situation on Lough Currane was really no different.

I would have to take the boat back some six miles to the village and attend at the Doctor's, that is if he was available. I was glad I would not have to row and I was thankful when the small 5 hp outboard engine fired on the first pull. But what a terrible waste of good fishing time, particularly as it seemed that the sea trout were on the take! As I motored slowly out of the bay, a thought occurred to me; there was, indeed, a possible alternative to returning to the village. Yes, there are many Doctors who fish (and at one time one of my best fishing friends was a Doctor). There was a boat some hundreds of yards ahead of me drifting into the bay. I wondered: 'could one or other of the two occupants be a Doctor? Well, it is certainly worth a try, so here goes'.

So as not to spook their water, I motored slowly to a position some hundred yards to the side of their boat, thus taking a fairly wide sweep to come up behind them, slackening speed as I did so. When well within hailing distance I stopped the engine and said in not too loud a voice, since I was talking down wind, as it were: 'excuse me, please, would either of you Gentlemen be a Doctor?' (expecting a negative reply).

The two occupants of the boat had already looked round at me when they heard my engine cut, so you can imagine my complete surprise when the older of the two relatively young men retorted: 'yes, we both are – what can we do for you?' The Doctors, of course, appreciated my amazement and when we had locked the two boats together I was invited into their 'boat-surgery', whereupon I showed them my affected finger. The older man, again, took the initiative and said: 'no problem – we shall have this out in five seconds flat'. He had already spotted my artery forceps attached to an extending lanyard and stuck in my fishing waistcoat. (This tool was given to me as a present by my Doctor fishing friend some years earlier and was now used as a hook disgorger – and very efficient too). One flick of the wrist and the hook was out. 'Let it bleed quite a lot and then suck it – gets rid of bacteria, you know', he said, his face showing as much pleasure as I knew mine was. In thanking them I asked whether they would be doing any après-fishing in the 'Butler Arms' later on that evening – but no, they had to drive home that night – they were operating in the morning!

Fools in the water

There came one day an English visitor to a top-grade and expensive hotel in the Scottish highlands for a few days' fishing on an excellent salmon river. He was pleasantly welcomed at reception by a pretty young lassie: 'Let me see,' she enquired, 'you must be Mr Enoch Mutchbrass from Little Puddlington-on-Sea?' 'Aye, that's right', he replied. 'The wife and I retired there after I left t'mill. Quiet place; not like Brashpool'. 'You are here for the fishing, sir', the receptionist confirmed. 'Aye, that's right, haven't had a lot of time for fishing up to now – first season, you know'. 'You are on beat 7 tomorrow and Alastair MacGreggor will be your ghillie. He'll be there at 10am. He's one of the best, sir'. 'Don't go much on ghillies myself', replied Mutchbrass. 'Seem a bit bossy to me'. 'The porter has taken up your bags, sir'. 'Thanks very much and good day to you'.

Next morning, Alastair was on the river bank at the upstream end of beat 7 at precisely 10 o'clock. He studied the water and sky and shook his head. The silence was soon broken by the purring of the engine of a large expensive motor car gleaming bright in the April sunshine. Although not a greatly travelled man, Alastair MacGreggor knew a Rolls when he saw one. The driver prised his well-nourished body from the comfortable leather seat, through the door and out on to the soft green grass.

Conscious of his responsibilities, Alastair leapt forward and gave his charge a helping hand as polished brown shoes found their footing on the uneven ground.

'Good mor--rning, sir---'. 'Good morning, MacGreggor, what are the prospects?' 'Not too good, but it all depends', replied the ghillie. Mutchbrass considered he wouldn't enquire as to what it depended on! In any case he wanted to get stuck into the fishing as soon as possible. 'I'll tell you what I want you to do, MacGreggor. The gear is in the boot and I would like you to put up the new Hardy built-cane salmon rod with the St Aidan reel and the floating line, a 15lb leader and a No 6 Blue Charm.'

Mutchbrass had learned about salmon flies from the man in the fishing tackle shop and he knew about weather because he had enjoyed the conducted tour of the meteorological reporting station at Valentia in County Kerry when he and his wife visited Ireland many years ago. He had read about the weather in books as well, and knew that you should use a bright fly on a bright day and a dark fly on a dull day.

Alastair soon had the rod assembled, the reel attached and the leader joined to the line. He approached the master. 'Ye'll nae catch a fish on a Blue Charm todee, sir---'. Mutchbrass was a little taken aback. He had not been contradicted like that for a long time. Mutchbrass stood his ground and in no uncertain manner made clear his views on the proper relationship of master and servant and insisted on his right to make his own choice of salmon fly. MacGreggor quietly obeyed. While he tied on the No 6 Blue Charm, Mutchbrass donned oiled Arran stockings and his newly purchased thigh waders with the specially built soles to prevent him slipping in the water. Alastair handed him the rod and patiently watched the corpulent form enter the fast-moving heavy water. Mutchbrass had read in one of his fishing books that the thing to do was to cast the fly 45° across and down and wait for it to come round and reach its limit. Having taken a course at the Hardy School of Casting under their senior instructor, he had indeed more than just a rudimentary knowledge of what to do.

After making two false casts to gain confidence, the fly went out like a dream over one of the salmon lies the ghillie had pointed out to him. There was a swirl, Mutchbrass raised his rod top slightly as he had been taught and the line went tight. He was into a salmon. MacGreggor said nothing. The strong fresh-run fish was fighting for its very life as yards of line were torn off as the reel screamed. Mutchbrass kept the line tight otherwise letting the salmon go when it wanted but reeling in fast when the fish came towards him. Just like it said in the book. There was, however, one nasty moment when the salmon on its second or third run had ideas of heading off downstream into the turbulent heavy water. Mutchbrass was still in command of the situation and was containing the large fish in all its exertions. He really was doing well considering his very limited experience.

The ghillie continued to stand well back in complete silence and after what had seemed hours to Mutchbrass, (but only 18 minutes in truth), the fish began to tire. After a few minutes more the angler was virtually holding the fish beaten, slightly head up, in just a few feet of water. He signalled to the ghillie that he was ready for the tailer. MacGreggor jumped to his feet, grabbed the brand new instrument, primed, entered the water to the left of the Rod (Mutchbrass was in fact left handed) and with great care gently slipped the noose into the water and over the salmon's tail. With a slight twitch of the wrist, the noose tightened and then with a long hard pull the salmon was hauled out of the water tail first. The ghillie, in his own professional and inimitable way, thumb and fingers in its gills, carried the salmon, with the Rod following him up the bank to a position beyond which the fish would have no hope of flapping itself to freedom back into the water. During all this time not a word was exchanged between the two of them, but many a glance. The ghillie then took the priest and performed the last rites, whilst the gent produced, as if from nowhere, a brand new spring balance which was easy to read in the spring sunshine. The pointer showed 16lb all but 1oz.

Now Mutchbrass was not a conceited man, although a trifle brash one, for in improving his fortunes he had come up the hard way. 'What do you think of that, MacGreggor?' he asked, out of breath and as red faced as ever. Without even a look or a glance, the ghillie answered, staring hard at the pool which had yielded the fish. 'Sir---', he said in his own dour way, 'there are fools in the water as well as oot'.

Confucius, he say. . .

We have all heard of the Chinese philosopher and his famous sayings, some of them far too risqué to be repeated in polite society. There is, however, one in particular that I rather like.

Confucius was, of course, an experienced fisherman of many summers and after much practice at the art of fly-casting he came to the indisputable conclusion that: 'Fisherman catch more fish when the fly is in the water than when it is in the air'. False casting experts and long haul devotees, please copy.

EPILOGUE

Should William Lunn be looking down from heaven, where, no doubt at all, he is, it is sincerely trusted that he will affirm that not too many stones have been left unturned in the quest for the fly's (or bait's) proper presentation 'at the proper time' and the bringing forth of 'the proper results'.

APPENDIX 1

SEVEN DEADLY SINS OF GAME FISHING

(and how to avoid committing them) as related to
the seven senses of the fish family, *Salmonidae*.

1. Sense of sight

Thou shalt not, neither shall thy shadow nor that of thy rod, come within the vision of the fish .

Avoid parading in loud and colourful habit on a skyline and above all keep your shadow off the water, by ensuring that the sun is off your back.

2. Lateral line sense

Thou shalt not cause earth vibrations which are transmitted into the water.

Always tread lightly but firmly, and never stamp about on the bank or in a boat. Rubber cleated boots are better in a boat than those with hobnails, and kinder to the boat, of course. Fish feel the effects of under-water vibrations in the lateral line, certainly uncomfortably, if not, sometimes, painfully. The writer, however, betrays a hypocritical trait in this context, having regard to the disturbances related earlier and the vibrations which can be caused by rocks, dogs, gaudy spinners and an alder tree.

94

3. *Feeling sense*

Thou shalt not use a gaff, or in any other manner inflict more pain or discomfort than is absolutely unavoidable upon a fish in the process of landing it.
One should always have at hand an effective priest with which to administer the last rites, before even attempting to extract the hook from the fish's mouth or the fish from the net. A large net for boat fishing and a tailer for bank fishing (but not for sea trout, because of the non-rigid caudal fin or tail) is more efficient and kinder. In the case of undersized sea trout, kelts (recently spawned fish), smolts or parr, always wet the hands before touching the fish or extracting the hook (preferably with artery forceps) and return the fish gently to the water, when on an even keel (the fish not the fisherman). Never, never, throw a fish back into the water. Fish are easily damaged. Should a fish be bleeding, it must be killed, fish do not survive any significant loss of blood.

4. *Sense of smell*

Thou shalt wash thy hands before setting forth and not afterwards allow them to touch highly spiced food or support a pipe which has to be filled by hand with often vile-smelling or otherwise scented leaf, the odour of which can be transmitted to the fly when attaching it to the leader.

5. *Sense of hearing*

Thou shalt not shout in a loud voice on the bank or in a boat. Other people may find it offensive.

6. *Hygiene*

Thou shalt not throw, or otherwise discharge into the water, any offensive matter or material.

95

So do not throw into the water the remains of yesterday's packed lunch, or that of the day before.

7. *Mass control sense*

Thou shalt not, knowingly, cast into a pool or bay into which, on the previous days, as part of a stocking programme, trout have been released.

APPENDIX 2

SEVEN GOLDEN RULES OF GAME FISHING

1. *Do* obey the rules of the water, such as those relating to the close season, the permitted methods of fishing, bag limits and the return of undersized fish.

2. *Do not* poach upon another rod's beat or fish too close to another boat or bank angler, whether beats are shared or not.

3. *Do please* take your litter home and not leave it on the bankside or in the boat.

4. *Do not* leave open gates which were found closed, nor close gates which were found open.

5. *Do not* break down or otherwise destroy trees or shrubs, unnecessarily. An exception would be the breaking of a small branch to release an expensive bait or fly.

6. *Do*, at all times, adopt a happy and helpful attitude and disposition to your fellow fishermen and, of course, to the landowners upon whose property you are fishing.

7. *Do please* pass on to younger and less experienced fishermen, in addition to all others, the ethics of game fishing, the better they may be equipped and enabled to enjoy their chosen craft. Not only is the fishing to be enjoyed but the peace

and quietness of lovely countryside, the relaxation from city 'rat races' of all kinds and the satisfaction, with full knowledge of the effects the elements have upon the quarry, of having done all possible to achieve the aim.

Those seven points are perhaps the basis of the fisherman's code and all of us are the better for taking heed of it.

In the misquoted words of the Olympic motto: *It is better to have fished without result than not to have fished at all.*

APPENDIX 3

BUCHAN'S COLD SPELLS

(Usually accompanied by a sharp fall in barometric pressure)

February 7th to 14th
April 11th to 14th
May 9th to 14th June
June 29th to July 4th
August 6th to 11th
November 6th to 11th

and four of his warm periods:

May 22nd to 26th
July 12th to 15th
August 12th to 15th
December 3rd to 9th

APPENDIX 4

SIZE OF BAIT OR FLY

A trout will, in general, take an imitation of the natural fly which is hatching or falling at the time. Fly size is accepted as being just as, or even more important than, fly pattern.

A salmon, however, does not feed in fresh water but similar considerations, in general regarding size, also apply to salmon baits spun or trolled and to artificial flies.

1. *Water temperature* is, no doubt, the most important factor in fixing the optimum size of fly or bait to be used, since this, inter alia, controls the dissolved oxygen content of the water.

2. *The height of the river* also affects the size of bait or fly. The higher the water the larger the bait or fly, and conversely, the lower, the smaller; on the basis that underwater vision is reduced in high water and increased in low water.

3. *The speed of the current* is another factor affecting size of bait or fly. The faster the current the larger, and conversely the slower the current the smaller the optimum bait or fly to be used.

4. *The colour of the water* is the final factor affecting the optimum size of bait, fly hook or tube fly. It is really a question of underwater vision, on the basis that the more

coloured the water with suspended matter, the lower the range of fish vision; and therefore the larger the optimum size to be used. The clearer the water, the greater the range of vision and the smaller the optimum size to be used.

The following Temperature/Lure Table will certainly help as a guide:

Table A:

TEMPERATURE			SIZE	
°F	°C	Bait	Fly hook	Tube fly
34/35	2	3½"	7/0	2½"
36/37	3	3½"	6/0	2½"
38/39	4	3"	5/0	2"
40/41	5	3"	4/0	2"
42/43	6	2¾"	3/0	1¾"
44/45	7	2¾"	2/0	1¾"
46/47	8	2½"	1/0	1½"
48/49	9	2½"	1	1¼"
50/51	10	2¼"	2	1¼"
52/53	11	2¼"	3	1"
54/55	12	2"	4	1"
56/57	14	2"	5	1"
58/59	15	1¾"	6	¾"
60/61	16	1¾"	7	¾"
62/63	17	1½"	8	¾"
64/65	18	1½"	9	¾"

Adjustments to temperature/lure size scales in Table A.

Table B:

HEIGHT OF WATER	TEMPERATURE °F
Very High	Less 8
High	Less 6
Average	Less 4
Low	Less 2
Very Low	No adjustment.

Adjustments to temperature/lure size scales in Table A

Table C:

SPEED OF CURRENT	TEMPERATURE °F
Very Slow	Plus 8
Slow	Plus 6
Average	Plus 4
Fast	Plus 2
Very Fast	No adjustment

Adjustments to temperature/lure size scales in Table A

Table D:

COLOUR OF WATER	TEMPERATURE °F
Clear	Plus 6
Coloured	Plus 4
Dirty	Plus 2

Examples of how to use these tables to estimate the best sizes of Bait Fly Hook and Tube Fly in the prevailing conditions.

Early Season, say, February/March

Water temperature	38°F (4°C)
Height of river	High
Speed of current	Fast
Colour of water	Coloured

Table A (temperature only) will suggest:

Bait	Fly Hook	Tube Fly
3″	5/0	2″

Now turn to Tables B, C, and D and read off the adjustments to temperature as follows:

High water	Less 6°F
Fast current	Plus 2°F
Clear water	Plus 6°F
Net temperature adjustment	Plus 2°F

101

The net adjustment amounts to just 2°F and this means that we must now turn to Table A again and add 2°F to the water temperature of 38°F which gives a hypothetical figure of 40°F. This suggests:

Bait	Fly Hook	Tube Fly
3″	4/0	2″

So in this case the adjustment is minimal. However, a salmon will rarely rise to the fly when the water temperature is lower than 48°F.

Spring, say, April/May

Water temperature	50°F (10°C)
Height of river	Average
Speed of current	Average
Colour of water	Clear

Table A (temperature only) will suggest:

Bait	Fly Hook	Tube Fly
2¼″	2	1¼″

Now turn to Tables B, C and D and read off the adjustment to temperature as follows:

Average Height	Less 4°F
Average current	Plus 4°F
Colour of water – clear	Plus 6°F
Net temperature adjustment	Plus 6°F

Now turn to table A again and add 6°F to the water temperature figure of 50°F which will now give a hypothetical figure of 56°F. This suggests:

Bait	Fly Hook	Tube Fly
2″	5	1″

Summer, say, June/July (Just after a spate)

Water temperature	56°F (13°C)
Height of water	Very high
Speed of current	Very fast
Colour of water	Dirty

As before from Table A, we read off:

Bait	Fly Hook	Tube Fly
1¾"	6	¾"

And from Tables B, C and D:

Very high	Less 8°F
Very fast current	No adjustment
Dirty water	Plus 2°F
Net adjustment	Less 6°F

Now turn to Table A again and deduct 6°F from the actual water temperature figure of 56°F which will give a hypothetical temperature figure of 50°F.

Now read off the sizes as follows against 50°F which will be:

Bait	Fly Hook	Tube Fly
2¼"	2	1¼"

High summer, say, August/September

Water temperature	59°F (15°C)
Height of water	Low
Current	Average
Colour	Clear

Water temperature of 59°F (15°C) will suggest:

Bait	Fly Hook	Tube Fly
1¾"	6	¾"

Now turn to Tables B, C and D and read off the adjustment to temperature as follows:

Low water	Less 2°F
Average current	Less 4°F
Clear water	Plus 6°F
	No further adjustment

If we summarise the maximum effects of water height, current and colour, we find that:

1. The difference between very high and very low water is equivalent to a temperature rise of 8°F.
2. The difference between very slow and very fast current is equivalent to a temperature drop of 8°F.
3. The difference between clear and dirty water is equivalent to a temperature drop of 6°F.